Airplane Design

Part I: Preliminary Sizing of Airplanes

Dr. Jan Roskam

Ackers Distinguished Professor of Aerospace Engineering
The University of Kansas, Lawrence

2005

Design • Analysis • Research

1440 Wakarusa Drive, Suite 500 • Lawrence, Kansas 66049, U.S.A.

PUBLISHED BY

Design, Analysis and Research Corporation (*DARcorporation*)
1440 Wakarusa Drive, Suite 500
Lawrence, Kansas 66049
U.S.A.
Phone: (785) 832-0434
Fax: (785) 832-0524
e-mail: info@darcorp.com
http://www.darcorp.com

ISBN-13: 978-1-884885-42-6
ISBN-10: 1-884885-42-X

In all countries, sold and distributed by
Design, Analysis and Research Corporation
1440 Wakarusa Drive, Suite 500
Lawrence, Kansas 66049
U.S.A.

TABLE OF CONTENTS
==================

CASA 212

TABLE OF SYMBOLS

Symbol	Definition	Dimension
A	Aspect ratio	-----
a,b	Regression line constants defined by Eqn.(3.21)	-----
A, B	Regression line constants defined by Eqn.(2.16)	-----
c,d	Regression line constants defined by Eqn.(3.22)	-----
C	Fuel fraction parameter defined by Eqn.(2.31)	-----
c_f	Equivalent skin friction coefficient	-----
c_j	Specific fuel consumption	lbs/lbs/hr
c_p	Specific fuel consumption	lbs/hp/hr
C_D	Drag coefficient	-----
C_{D_0}	Zero lift drag coefficient	-----
CGR	Climb gradient, defined by Eqn.(3.28)	rad
CGRP	Climb gradient parameter, defined by Eqn.(3.30)	rad
C_L	Lift coefficient	-----
D	Drag	lbs
D(Alternate meaning)	$W_{PL} + W_{crew}$	lbs
D_p	Propeller diameter	ft
e	Oswald's efficiency factor	-----
E	Endurance	hours
$\bar{E}$	$\ln(W_i/W_{i+1})$, Eqns.(2.37 and 2.39)	-----
f	equivalent parasite area	ft^2
F	Weight sensitivity parameter, Eqn.(2.44)	lbs
FAR	Federal Air Regulation	-----
g	acceleration of gravity	ft/sec^2
h	altitude	ft

I_p	Power index, Eqn.(3.51)	$(hp/ft^2)^{1/3}$
k	number between 0 and 1	-----
k_1	constant in Eqn.(3.9)	sec^2/ft
k_2	constant in Eqn.(3.9)	-----
l_p	factor in k_2, see p.102	
L	Lift	lbs
L/D	Lift-to-drag ratio	-----
M_{ff}	Mission fuel fraction (M_{ff}= End weight/Begin weight)	none
n	Load factor	-----
nm	Nautical mile(6,076 ft)	nm
N	Number of engines	-----
P	Power, Horse-power (1hp = 550 ft.lbs/sec)	hp
P_{dl}	Parameter in $\sin\gamma$, Eqns.(3.38) and (3.39)	-----
P_s	Specific excess power	ft/sec
$\bar{q}$	dynamic pressure	psf
R	Range	nm or m
$\bar{R}$	$\ln(W_i/W_{i+1})$, Eqns.(2.36 and 2.38)	-----
RC	Rate of climb	fpm or fps
RCP	Rate-of-climb parameter, Eqns.(3.24) and (3.25)	hp/lbs
s	distance, used in take-off and landing equations with subscripts	ft
sm	Statute mile(5,280 ft)	sm
S	Wing area	ft^2
SHP	Shaft horsepower	hp_2
S_{wet}	Wetted area	ft^2
t	time	sec, min, hr
T	Thrust	lbs
TOP_{23}	FAR 23 Take-off parameter	$lbs^2/ft^2 hp$
TOP_{25}	FAR 25 Take-off parameter	lbs/ft^2

V	True airspeed	mph. fps. kts
wod, WOD	Wind over the deck	kts
W	Weight	lbs
X	T(hrust) or P(ower)	lbs or hp

Greek Symbols
==============

η_p	propeller efficiency	-----
π	product, or 3.142	-----
ρ	air density	slugs/ft^3
σ	air density ratio	-----
μ_G	ground friction coefficient	-----
δ	pressure ratio	-----
γ	flight path angle	deg or rad
$\dot{\psi}$	turn rate	rad/sec
θ	temperature ratio	-----
λ	bypass ratio	-----

Subscripts
==========

A	Approach
abs	absolute
cat	catapult
cl	climb
cr	cruise
crew	crew
E	Empty
f	flaps
ff	fuel fraction (see M_{ff})
F	Mission fuel
FEQ	Fixed equipment
FL	Field length
guess	guessed
h	altitude
L	Landing
LG	Landing, ground
LO	Lift-off
ltr	loiter
max	maximum
ME	Manufacturer's empty
MIF	Maximum internal fuel
OE	Operating empty
PA	Powered approach
PL	Payload
RC	Rate-of-climb

res	reserve, as in fuel reserve
reqd	required
s	stall
TO	Take-off
TOFL	Take-off field length
TOG	Take-off, ground
tent	tentative
tfo	trapped fuel and oil
used	used, as in fuel used
wet	wetted
wod	wind over the deck

Acronyms
========

AEO	All engines operating
Al-Li	Aluminum-Lithium
APU	Auxiliary power unit
ARALL	Aramid-Aluminum
C^3I	Communication, Control, Command, Intelligence
hp	horsepower
l.h.s.	left hand side
NA or N.A.	Not Applicable
OEI	One engine inoperative
OWE	Operating weight empty
RFP	Request for proposal
r.h.s.	right hand side
shp	shaft horsepower
sls	sealevel standard
TBP	Turboprop

BEECH DUCHESS

ACKNOWLEDGEMENT
================

Writing a book on airplane design is impossible without the supply of a large amount of data. The author is grateful to the following companies for supplying the raw data, manuals, sketches and drawings which made the book what it is:

Beech Aircraft Corporation
Boeing Commercial Airplane Company
Canadair
Cessna Aircraft Company
DeHavilland Aircraft Company of Canada
Gates Learjet Corporation
Lockheed Aircraft Corporation
McDonnell Douglas Corporation
Rinaldo Piaggio S.p.A.
Royal Netherlands Aircraft Factory, Fokker
SIAI Marchetti S.p.A.

A significant amount of airplane design information has been accumulated by the author over many years from the following magazines:

Interavia (Swiss, monthly)
Flight International (British, weekly)
Business and Commercial Aviation (USA, monthly)
Aviation Week and Space Technology (USA, weekly)
Journal of Aircraft (USA, AIAA, monthly)

The author wishes to acknowledge the important role played by these magazines in his own development as an aeronautical engineer. Aeronautical engineering students and graduates should read these magazines regularly.

PIPER T-1040

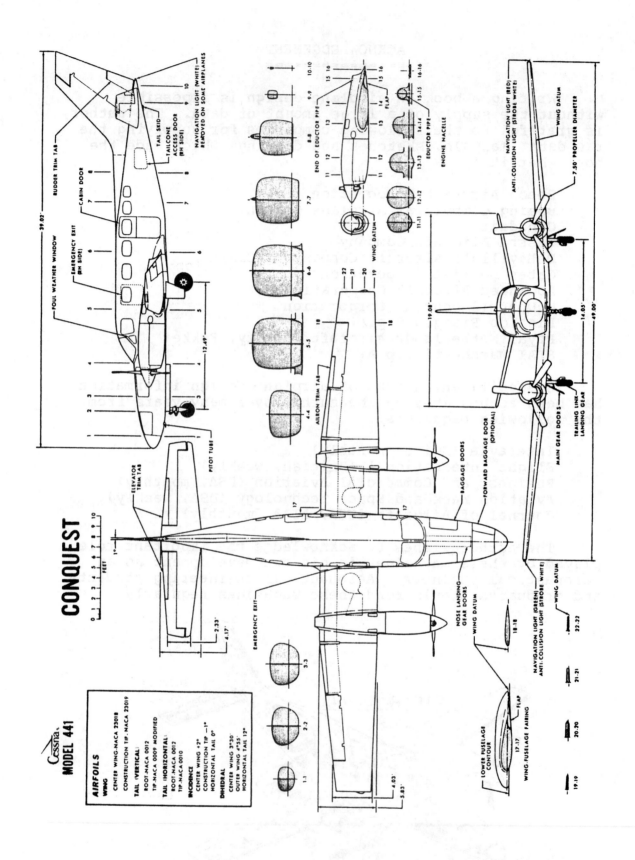

CONQUEST

Cessna.
MODEL 441

AIRFOILS

WING

CENTER WING-NACA 23018
CONSTRUCTION TIP. NACA 23019

TAIL (VERTICAL)

ROOT-NACA 0012
TIP-NACA 0009 MODIFIED

TAIL (HORIZONTAL)

ROOT-NACA 0012
TIP-NACA 0010

INCIDENCE

CENTER WING +2°
CONSTRUCTION TIP —1°
HORIZONTAL TAIL 0°

DIHEDRAL

CENTER WING 3°30'
OUTER WING 4°55'
HORIZONTAL TAIL 12°

1. INTRODUCTION
================

        The purpose of this series of books on Airplane
Design is to familiarize aerospace engineering students
with the methodology and decision making involved in the
process of designing airplanes.
        To design an airplane it is necessary that a
mission specification for the airplane is available.
Airplane mission specifications come about in different
ways, depending on the type of airplane and sometimes
depending on the customer.
        Figure 1.1 illustrates several paths along which
mission specifications can evolve. The reader will note,
that the words preliminary sizing and preliminary design
appear in Figure 1.1. This series of books concentrates
on these phases of airplane design.
        Many airplanes never make it beyond the initial or
preliminary design phase. In fact, most don't. What
happens beyond the preliminary design phase depends to a
large extent on the results obtained during preliminary
design and on the real or perceived market interest
afterward.
        If, as a result of the preliminary design studies a
specific need can be met, then full scale development of
the airplane can follow. If, as a result of the
preliminary design studies certain problem areas are
discovered (such as specific technological deficiencies
which need development to be corrected, or such as a
lacking data base) then a research and development
program can be initiated aimed at overcoming these
problems. Eventually, with the problems solved, a final
mission specification is evolved which then can lead to
full scale development.
        If it becomes evident during the research program,
that the problems cannot be solved in a reasonable time
frame or at a reasonable cost, the subject design can be
dropped or modified.
        Figure 1.2 illustrates the preliminary design
process as it is covered in this series of books.
        The series of books is organized as follows:

        PART I: PRELIMINARY SIZING OF AIRPLANES
        PART II: PRELIMINARY CONFIGURATION DESIGN AND
                    INTEGRATION OF THE PROPULSION SYSTEM
        PART III: LAYOUT DESIGN OF COCKPIT, FUSELAGE, WING
                    AND EMPENNAGE: CUTAWAYS AND INBOARD
                    PROFILES
        PART IV: LAYOUT DESIGN OF LANDING GEAR AND SYSTEMS
        PART V: COMPONENT WEIGHT ESTIMATION

PART VI: PRELIMINARY CALCULATION OF AERODYNAMIC,
             THRUST AND POWER CHARACTERISTICS
PART VII: DETERMINATION OF STABILITY, CONTROL AND
             PERFORMANCE CHARACTERISTICS: FAR AND
             MILITARY REQUIREMENTS
PART VIII: AIRPLANE COST ESTIMATION: DESIGN,
             DEVELOPMENT, MANUFACTURING AND OPERATING

The purpose of PART I is to present a rapid method for the preliminary sizing of an airplane to a given mission specification.

Preliminary sizing is defined as the process which results in the numerical definition of the following airplane design parameters:

* Gross Take-off Weight, W_{TO}

* Empty Weight, W_E

* Mission Fuel Weight, W_F

* Maximum Required Take-off Thrust, T_{TO} or Take-off Power, P_{TO}

* Wing Area, S and Wing Aspect Ratio, A

* Maximum Required Lift Coefficient (Clean), $C_{L_{max}}$

* Maximum Required Lift Coefficient for Take-off, $C_{L_{max_{TO}}}$

* Maximum Required Lift Coefficient for Landing, $C_{L_{max_L}}$ or $C_{L_{max_{PA}}}$

It is assumed in this book that a mission specification for the airplane is available. Typical parameters which are numerically defined in a mission specification are:

* Payload and type of payload
* Range and/or loiter requirements
* Cruise speed and altitude
* Field length for take-off and for landing
* Fuel reserves
* Climb requirements
* Maneuvering requirements
* Certification base (For example: Experimental, FAR 23, FAR 25 or Military)

Some mission specifications will contain much more detail than others. This depends on the customer who wrote the specification and on the amount of design flexibility this customer wants the airplane designer to have.

The sizing methods presented in this book appear in the following sequence:

Chapter 2: Estimating take-off gross weight, W_{TO}, empty weight, W_E and mission fuel weight, W_F.

Chapter 3: Estimating wing area, S, wing aspect ratio, A, take-off thrust, T_{TO} and maximum lift coefficients, $C_{L_{max}}$, $C_{L_{max_{TO}}}$ and $C_{L_{max_L}}$.

Chapter 4 provides a user's guide through the preliminary sizing process.

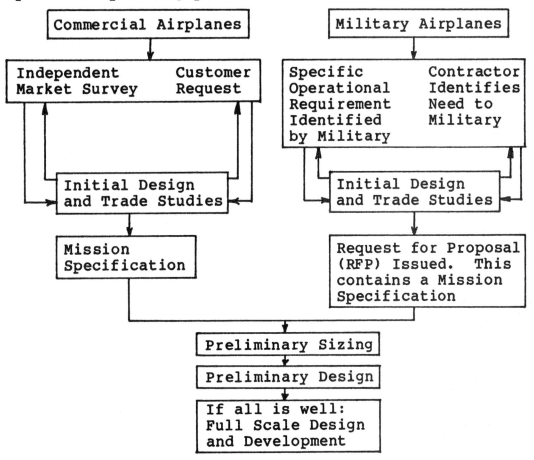

Figure 1.1 Example of Evolution of a Mission Specification and its Relation to Preliminary Sizing and Design

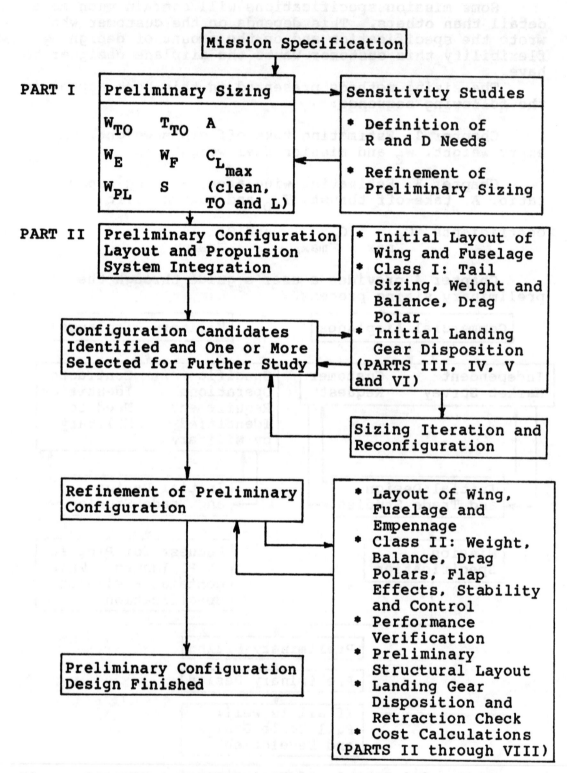

Figure 1.2 The Preliminary Design Process As Covered In Parts I Through VIII Of 'AIRPLANE DESIGN'

2. ESTIMATING TAKE-OFF GROSS WEIGHT, W_{TO}, EMPTY WEIGHT, W_E, AND MISSION FUEL WEIGHT, W_F

Airplanes must normally meet very stringent range, endurance, speed and cruise speed objectives while carrying a given payload. It is important, to be able to predict the minimum airplane weight and fuel weight needed to accomplish a given mission.

For a given mission specification, this chapter presents a rapid method for estimating:

* Take-off gross weight, W_{TO}

* Empty weight, W_E

* Mission fuel weight, W_F

The method applies to the following twelve types of airplanes:

1. Homebuilt Propeller Driven Airplanes
2. Single Engine Propeller Driven Airplanes
3. Twin Engine Propeller Driven Airplanes
4. Agricultural Airplanes
5. Business Jets
6. Regional Turbopropeller Driven Airplanes
7. Transport Jets
8. Military Trainers
9. Fighters
10. Military Patrol, Bomb and Transport Airplanes
11. Flying Boats, Amphibious and Float Airplanes
12. Supersonic Cruise Airplanes

2.1 GENERAL OUTLINE OF THE METHOD

A convenient way to break down W_{TO} is as follows:

$$W_{TO} = W_{OE} + W_F + W_{PL} \qquad (2.1)$$

where:

W_{OE} is the airplane operating weight empty,

W_F is the mission fuel weight,

W_{PL} is the payload weight.

The operating weight empty, W_{OE} (also called OWE),

is frequently written as follows:

$$W_{OE} = W_E + W_{tfo} + W_{crew} \qquad (2.2)$$

where:

W_E is the empty weight,

W_{tfo} is the weight of all trapped (=unusable) fuel and oil,

W_{crew} is the weight of the crew required to operate the airplane.

It must be kept in mind, that the empty weight, W_E

is sometimes broken down in the following manner:

$$W_E = W_{ME} + W_{FEQ} \qquad (2.3)$$

where:

W_{ME} is the manufacturers empty weight, sometimes referred to as the green weight,

W_{FEQ} is the fixed equipment weight.

Fixed equipment weight can include such items as:

* avionics equipment
* airconditioning equipment
* special radar equipment
* auxiliary power unit (APU)
* furnishings and interiors
* other equipment needed to operate the airplane during its intended mission

At this junction, two key points must be made:

Point 1: It is not difficult to estimate the required mission fuel weight W_F from very basic

considerations. This will be shown in Section 2.4.

Point 2: There exists a linear relationship between $\log_{10} W_{TO}$ and $\log_{10} W_E$ for the twelve types of airplanes

mentioned before. Graphical evidence for this will be shown in Section 2.5.

Based on these two points, the process of estimating

values for W_{TO}, W_E and W_F consists of seven steps:

Step 1. Determine the mission payload weight, W_{PL} (Section 2.2).

Step 2. Guess a likely value of take-off weight, $W_{TO_{guess}}$ (Section 2.3).

Step 3. Determine the mission fuel weight, W_F (Section 2.4).

Step 4. Calculate a tentative value for W_{OE} from:

$$W_{OE_{tent}} = W_{TO_{guess}} - W_F - W_{PL} \qquad (2.4)$$

Step 5. Calculate a tentative value for W_E from:

$$W_{E_{tent}} = W_{OE_{tent}} - W_{tfo} - W_{crew} \qquad (2.5)$$

Although W_{tfo} can amount to as much as 0.5%

or more of W_{TO} for some airplanes, it is

often neglected at this stage in the design process.
How to determine the numerical value for W_{crew} is discussed in Section 2.2.

Step 6. Find the allowable value of W_E from Section 2.5.

Step 7. Compare the values for $W_{E_{tent}}$ and for

W_E as obtained from Steps 5 and 6. Next,

make an adjustment to the value of $W_{TO_{guess}}$

and repeat Steps 3 through 6. Continue this
process until the values of $W_{E_{tent}}$ and W_E

agree with each other to within some pre-se-
lected tolerance. A tolerance of 0.5% is u-
sually sufficient at this design level.

Sections 2.2 through 2.5 contain detailed methods
for estimating W_{PL}, W_{TO} and W_F. Section 2.6 applies

the stepwise methodology to three types of airplanes.

NOTE WELL: Instead of using this procedure the reader may use Eqn.(2.24) to solve for W_{TO} directly! The

convergence properties of this method are discussed in
Appendix A.

2.2 DETERMINATION OF MISSION PAYLOAD WEIGHT, W_{PL}, AND CREW WEIGHT, W_{crew}

Mission payload weight, W_{PL} is normally specified in the mission specification. This payload weight usually consists of one or more of the following:

1. Passengers and baggage
2. Cargo
3. Military loads such as ammunition, bombs, missiles and a variety of stores or pods which are usually carried externally and therefore affect the airplane drag

For passengers in a commercial airplane an average weight of 175 lbs per person and 30 lbs of baggage is a reasonable assumption for short to medium distance flights. For long distance flights, the baggage weight should be assumed to be 40 lbs. per person.

The crew weight, W_{crew} is found from the following considerations:

Commercial:
The crew consists of the cockpit crew and the cabin crew. The number of people in each crew depends on the airplane and its mission. It depends also on the total number of passengers carried. Reference 8, FAR 91.215 specifies the minimum number of cabin crew members required.

For crew members an average weight of 175 lbs plus 30 lbs of baggage is a reasonable assumption.

Military:
For military crew members a weight of 200 lbs should be assumed because of extra gear carried.

Caution:
Because FAR 23 certified airplanes (Types 2 and 3) are frequently operated by owner/pilots it is not unusual to define the crew weight as part of the payload in these cases.

2.3 GUESSING A LIKELY VALUE OF TAKE-OFF WEIGHT, $W_{TO_{guess}}$

An initial 'guess' of the value of take-off weight, $W_{TO_{guess}}$ is usually obtained by comparing the mission specification of the airplane with the mission capabilities of similar airplanes listed in Reference 9. If no reasonable comparison can be made (perhaps because the specification calls for a type of airplane never before conceived) then it will be necessary to make an arbitrary 'guess'.

2.4 DETERMINATION OF MISSION FUEL WEIGHT, W_F

In Section 2.1, Point 1 indicated that it is not difficult to estimate a value for W_F from basic

considerations. This section presents a method for doing just that.

Mission fuel weight, W_F can be written as:

$$W_F = W_{F_{used}} + W_{F_{res}} \qquad (2.6)$$

where:

$W_{F_{used}}$ is the fuel actually used during the mission,

$W_{F_{res}}$ are the fuel reserves required for the mission.

Fuel reserves are normally specified in the mission specification. They are also specified in those FAR's which regulate the operation of passenger transports. Fuel reserves are generally specified in one or more of the following types:

1. as a fraction of $W_{F_{used}}$
2. as a requirement for additional range so that an alternate airport can be reached
3. as a requirement for (additional) loiter time

To determine $W_{F_{used}}$, the fuel weight actually used during the mission, the so-called fuel-fraction method will be used. In this method the airplane mission is broken down into a number of mission phases. The fuel used during each phase is found from a simple calculation or estimated on the basis of experience.

The fuel-fraction method will be illustrated by applying it to an arbitrary airplane. Figure 2.1 defines the mission profile for this airplane.

It will be observed that the mission profile is broken down into a number of mission phases. Each phase has a number. Each phase also has a begin weight and an end weight associated with it.

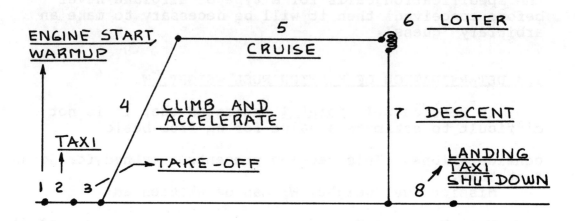

Figure 2.1 Mission Profile for an Arbitrary Airplane

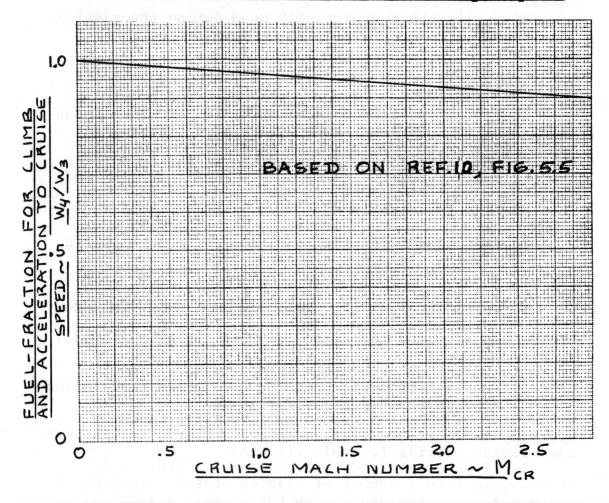

Figure 2.2 Fuel Fraction for Phase 4 of Figure 2.1

The following definition is important:

Definition: The fuel-fraction for each phase is defined as the ratio of end weight to begin weight.

The next step is to assign a numerical value to the fuel-fraction corresponding to each mission phase. This is done as follows:

Phase 1: Engine start and warm-up.
Begin weight is W_{TO}. End weight is W_1.

The fuel-fraction for this phase is by previous definition given by: W_1/W_{TO}.

Table 2.1 provides a guide for determining this fraction for twelve types of airplanes.

Phase 2: Taxi.
Begin weight is W_1. End weight is W_2.

The fuel-fraction for this phase is W_2/W_1.

Table 2.1 provides a guide for determining this fraction for twelve types of airplanes.

Phase 3: Take-off.
Begin weight is W_2. End weight is W_3.

The fuel-fraction for this phase is W_3/W_2.

Table 2.1 provides a guide for determining this fraction for twelve types of airplanes.

Phase 4: Climb to cruise altitude and accelerate to cruise speed.
Begin weight is W_3. End weight is W_4.

The fuel fraction for this phase, W_4/W_3 may be determined directly from

Figure 2.2.
However, in some cases it is desirable to calculate this fraction from Breguet's equation for endurance (Ref.14):

Table 2.1 Suggested Fuel-Fractions For Several Mission Phases
==

Mission Phase No.(See Fig.2.1) Airplane Type:	Engine Start, Warm-up 1	Taxi 2	Take-off 3	Climb 4	Descent 7	Landing, Taxi, Shutdown 8
1. Homebuilt	0.998	0.998	0.998	0.995	0.995	0.995
2. Single Engine	0.995	0.997	0.998	0.992	0.993	0.993
3. Twin Engine	0.992	0.996	0.996	0.990	0.992	0.992
4. Agricultural	0.996	0.995	0.996	0.998	0.999	0.998
5. Business Jets	0.990	0.995	0.995	0.980	0.990	0.992
6. Regional TBP's	0.990	0.995	0.995	0.985	0.985	0.995
7. Transport Jets	0.990	0.990	0.995	0.980	0.990	0.992
8. Military Trainers	0.990	0.990	0.990	0.980	0.990	0.995
9. Fighters	0.990	0.990	0.990	0.96-0.90	0.990	0.995
10. Mil.Patrol, Bomb, Transport	0.990	0.990	0.995	0.980	0.990	0.992
11. Flying Boats, Amphibious, Float Airplanes	0.992	0.990	0.996	0.985	0.990	0.990
12. Supersonic Cruise	0.990	0.995	0.995	0.92-0.87	0.985	0.992

Notes: 1. The numbers in this table are based on experience or on judgment.
2. There is no substitute for common sense! If and when common sense so dictates, the reader should substitute other values for the fractions suggested in this table.

<u>for propeller-driven airplanes:</u>

$$E_{cl} = 375(1/V_{cl})(\eta_p/c_p)_{cl}(L/D)_{cl}\ln(W_3/W_4) \qquad (2.7)$$

<u>Note:</u> V_{cl} in Eqn.(2.7) is in mph.

If the fuel-fraction for the climb phase is to be calculated in this manner then it is necessary to estimate average values during the climb for V_{cl}, for $(\eta_p/c_p)_{cl}$ and

for $(L/D)_{cl}$. Table 2.2 provides a guide

from which these quantities can be found.

<u>for jet airplanes:</u>

$$E_{cl} = (1/c_j)_{cl}(L/D)_{cl}\ln(W_3/W_4) \qquad (2.8)$$

If the fuel-fraction for the climb phase is to be calculated in this manner then it is necessary to estimate average values during the climb for $c_{j_{cl}}$, and for $(L/D)_{cl}$.
Table 2.2 provides a guide from which it is possible to find these quantities.

E_{cl} in Eqn.(2.8) is equal to the time

to climb, usually expressed as a fraction of an hour. This can be found in turn by assuming a value for the average rate-of-climb. The altitude at the end of the climb (usually referred to as the cruise or loiter altitude) is normally provided in the airplane mission specification. Methods for rapid evaluation of climb performance are discussed in Chapter 3.

Phase 5: Cruise.
Begin weight is W_4. End weight is W_5.

The ratio W_5/W_4 can be estimated from

Breguet's range equation (Ref.14), which can be written as follows:

Table 2.2 Suggested Values For L/D, c_j, η_p, And For c_p For Several Mission Phases

Airplane Type	Cruise				Loiter			
Mission Phase No. (See Fig.2.1)	L/D	c_j lbs/lbs/hr (5)	c_p lbs/hp/hr	η_p	L/D	c_j lbs/lbs/hr (6)	c_p lbs/hp/hr	η_p
1. Homebuilt	8-10*		0.6-0.8	0.7	10-12		0.5-0.7	0.6
2. Single Engine	8-10		0.5-0.7	0.8	10-12		0.5-0.7	0.7
3. Twin Engine	8-10		0.5-0.7	0.82	9-11		0.5-0.7	0.72
4. Agricultural	5-7		0.5-0.7	0.82	8-10		0.5-0.7	0.72
5. Business Jets	10-12	0.5-0.9			12-14	0.4-0.6		
6. Regional TBP's	11-13		0.4-0.6	0.85	14-16		0.4-0.6	0.77
7. Transport Jets	13-15	0.5-0.9			14-18	0.4-0.6		
8. Military Trainers	8-10		0.5-1.0	0.82	10-14		0.4-0.6	0.77
9. Fighters	4-7	0.6-1.4		0.82	6-9	0.6-0.8		0.77
10. Mil.Patrol, Bomb, Transport	13-15	0.5-0.9	0.4-0.7	0.82	14-18		0.4-0.6	0.77
11. Flying Boats, Amphibious, Float Airplanes	10-12	0.5-0.9	0.5-0.7	0.82	13-15		0.4-0.6	0.77
12. Supersonic Cruise	4-6	0.7-1.5			7-9	0.6-0.8		

Notes:
1. The numbers in this table represent ranges based on existing engines.
2. There is no substitute for common sense! If and when actual data are available, these should be used.
3. A good estimate for L/D can be made with the drag polar method of Sub-section 3.4.1.
* Homebuilts with smooth exteriors and/or high wing loadings can have L/D values which are considerably higher.

for propeller-driven airplanes:

$$R_{cr} = 375(\eta_p/c_p)_{cr}(L/D)_{cr}\ln(W_4/W_5) \qquad (2.9)$$

Note: R_{cr} in Eqn.(2.9) is in stat. miles.

for jet airplanes:

$$R_{cr} = (V/c_j)_{cr}(L/D)_{cr}\ln(W_4/W_5) \qquad (2.10)$$

Note, that R_{cr} is usually expressed in n.m.

Values for $(\eta_p/c_p)_{cr}$, for $c_{j_{cr}}$ and

for $(L/D)_{cr}$ may again be obtained from

Table 2.2. Values for R_{cr} and for V_{cr} are

usually given in the mission specification.

Phase 6: Loiter.
Begin weight is W_5. End weight is W_6.

The fuel-fraction W_6/W_5 can be found

with the help of Breguet's endurance
equation:

for propeller-driven airplanes:

$$E_{ltr} = \qquad\qquad\qquad\qquad\qquad (2.11)$$
$$375(1/V_{ltr})(\eta_p/c_p)_{ltr}(L/D)_{ltr}\ln(W_5/W_6)$$

Note: V_{ltr} in Eqn.(2.11) is in mph (=smph).

for jet airplanes:

$$E_{ltr} = (1/c_{j_{ltr}})(L/D)_{ltr}\ln(W_5/W_6) \qquad (2.12)$$

Note, that E_{ltr} is usually expressed in

hours. Values for $(\eta_p/c_p)_{ltr}$, for $c_{j_{ltr}}$ and

for $(L/D)_{ltr}$ can be obtained again from

Table 2.2. Values for V_{ltr} and for E are

often given in the mission specification.

Phase 7: Descent.

Begin weight is W_6. End weight is W_7.

The fuel-fraction W_7/W_6 may be found

from Table 2.1.

Phase 8: Landing, taxi and shut-down.

Begin weight is W_7. End weight is W_8.

The fuel-fraction W_8/W_7 may be found

from Table 2.1.

It is now possible to calculate the mission fuel-fraction, M_{ff} from:

$$M_{ff} = (W_1/W_{TO}) \prod_{i=1}^{i=7} (W_{i+1}/W_i) \qquad (2.13)$$

The fuel used during the mission, $W_{F_{used}}$ can be found from:

$$W_{F_{used}} = (1 - M_{ff})W_{TO} \qquad (2.14)$$

The value for mission fuel weight, W_F can finally be determined from:

$$W_F = (1 - M_{ff})W_{TO} + W_{F_{res}} \qquad (2.15)$$

Specific examples of how this fuel-fraction method can be applied to airplanes are presented in section 2.6.

2.5 FINDING THE ALLOWABLE VALUE FOR W_E

In Section 2.1, Point 2 raised the issue of the existence of a linear relationship between $\log_{10} W_E$ and $\log_{10} W_{TO}$. Once such a relationship is established, it should be easy to obtain W_E from W_{TO}.

Figures 2.3 through 2.14 demonstrate that such relationships indeed exist. The data presented in Figures 2.3 through 2.14 are based on Tables 2.3 through 2.14. These tables in turn are based on data found in Reference 9 or on data obtained directly from airplane manufacturers.

The trend lines in Figures 2.3 through 2.14 were established with the help of a regression analysis. The reader should consider these trend lines to be a fair representation of the 'state-of-the-art' of airplane design. It is desirable to have as small a value for W_E for any given value of W_{TO}. Therefore, it is reasonable to assume, that a manufacturer will always try to make W_E as small as possible for any given take-off weight, W_{TO}.

For that reason, at any value of W_{TO} in Figures 2.3 through 2.14, the corresponding value of W_E should be viewed as the 'minimum allowable' value at the current 'state-of-the-art' of airplane design.

Several ways for finding W_E from W_{TO} present themselves:

1. For a given value of W_{TO} as obtained from Step 2 in Section 2.1, the allowable value for W_E can be read from Figures 2.3 through 2.14.

2. For a given value of W_{TO} as obtained from Step 2 in Section 2.1, the allowable value for W_E can be found by interpolation from Tables 2.3 through 2.14.

3. For a given value of W_{TO} as obtained from Step 2 in Section 2.1, the allowable value for W_E can be found from the following equation:

$$W_E = \text{inv.} \log_{10}\{(\log_{10}W_{TO} - A)/B\} \qquad (2.16)$$

This equation represents the regression lines shown in Figures 2.3 through 2.14. Numerical values for the quantities A and B are listed in Table 2.15.

<u>An important note of caution</u>:

The primary structures of most of the airplanes listed in Figures 2.3 to 2.14 and Tables 2.3 t0 2.14 are manufactured mainly of metallic materials: mostly pre-1986 aluminum alloys. Exceptions are indicated.

If the reader wishes to obtain an estimate of W_E for an airplane which is to be made of composite materials, or of modern aluminum based materials such as Al-Li and/or ARALL, the following guidelines should be observed:

1.) Determine which airplane components are to be made from the new materials.

2.) Determine an average value for W_{new}/W_{old} for the new airplane from Table 2.16. The allowable value of W_E as found from Figures 2.3 to 2.14 must now be multiplied by W_{new}/W_{old}, as listed in Table 2.16.

An alternate approach is to determine a 'new' value for the regression (intercept) coefficient 'A' which appears in Eqn.(2.16). Appendix B gives a simple method for doing this.

The reader should keep in mind, that non-primary structures, such as floors, fairings, flaps, control surfaces and interior furnishings, have been manufactured from composites and/or other advanced materials for several years. Claims of weight reductions relative to the airplanes in Figures 2.3 through 2.14 should therefore be made with great caution.

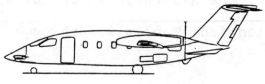

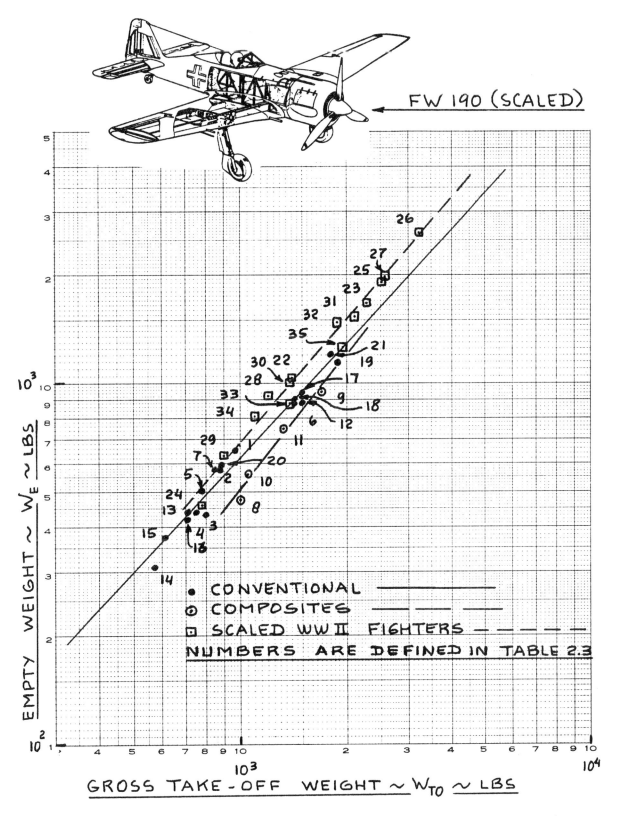

FW 190 (SCALED)

CONVENTIONAL ———
COMPOSITES – – –
SCALED WW II FIGHTERS —–—–—
NUMBERS ARE DEFINED IN TABLE 2.3

EMPTY WEIGHT ~ W_E ~ LBS

GROSS TAKE-OFF WEIGHT ~ W_{TO} ~ LBS

Figure 2.3 Weight Trends for Homebuilt Propeller Driven
Airplanes

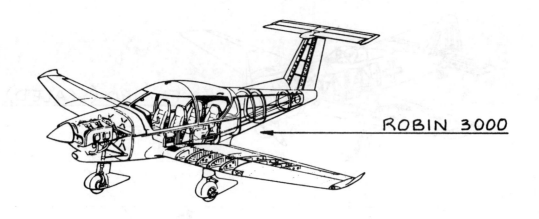

ROBIN 3000

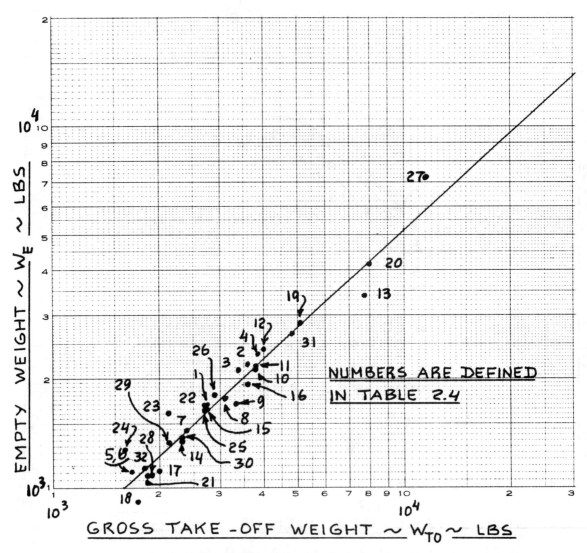

NUMBERS ARE DEFINED IN TABLE 2.4

Figure 2.4 Weight Trends for Single Engine Propeller Driven Airplanes

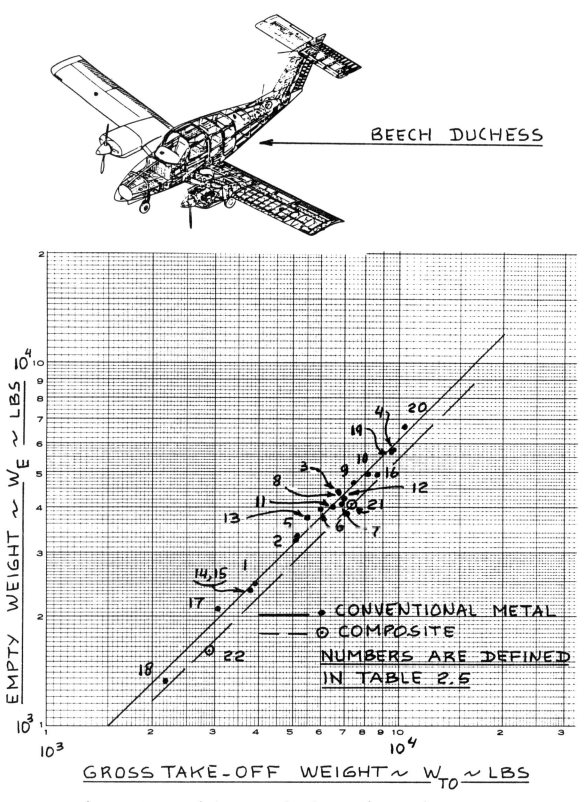

BEECH DUCHESS

Figure 2.5 Weight Trends for Twin Engine Propeller Driven Airplanes

——— • CONVENTIONAL METAL

— — ○ COMPOSITE

NUMBERS ARE DEFINED IN TABLE 2.5

EMPTY WEIGHT ~ W_E ~ LBS

GROSS TAKE-OFF WEIGHT ~ W_{TO} ~ LBS

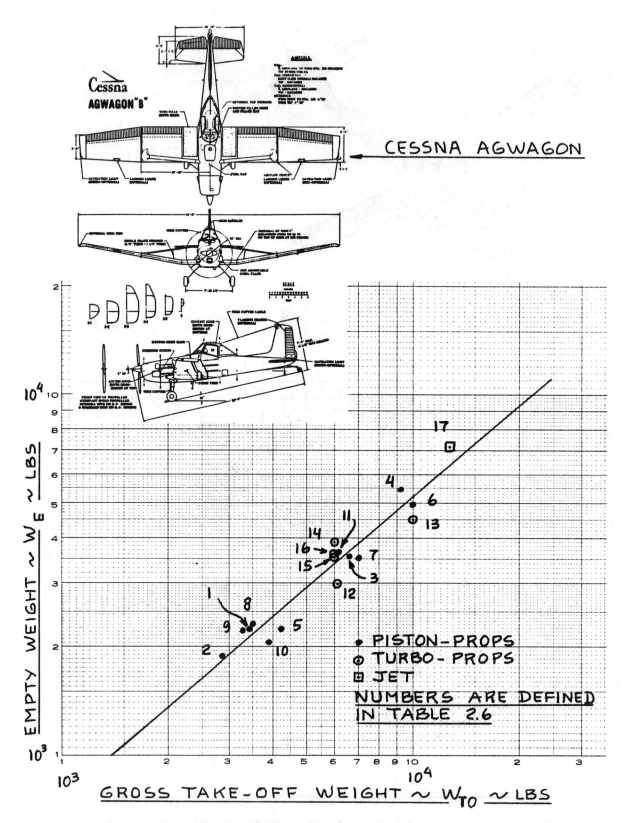

CESSNA AGWAGON

PISTON-PROPS
TURBO-PROPS
JET

NUMBERS ARE DEFINED
IN TABLE 2.6

Figure 2.6 Weight Trends for Agricultural Airplanes

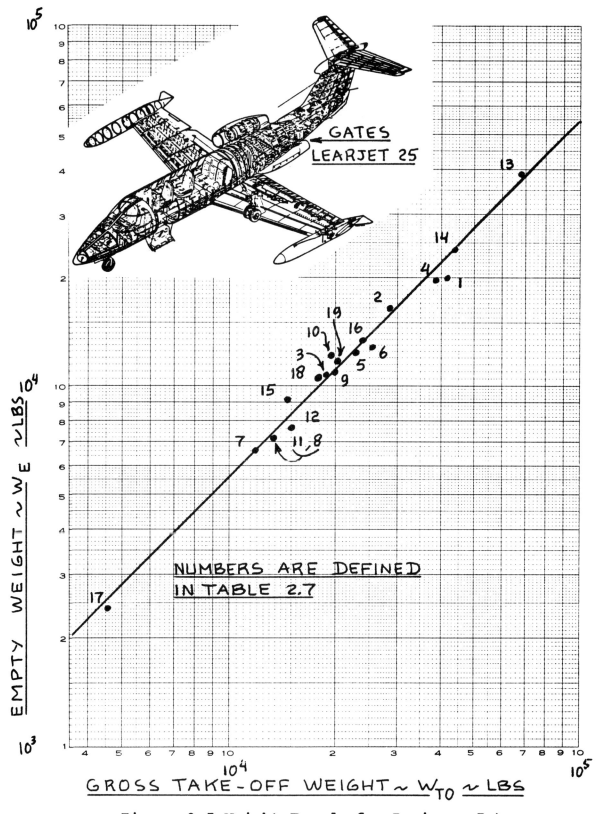

GATES
LEARJET 25

NUMBERS ARE DEFINED
IN TABLE 2.7

EMPTY WEIGHT ~ W_E ~ LBS

GROSS TAKE-OFF WEIGHT ~ W_TO ~ LBS

Figure 2.7 Weight Trends for Business Jets

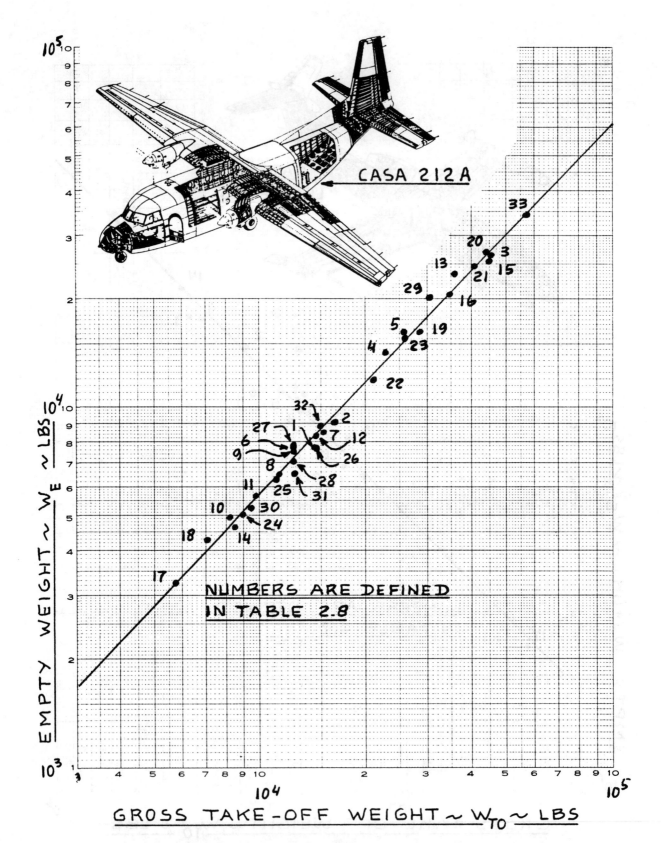

NUMBERS ARE DEFINED
IN TABLE 2.8

Figure 2.8 Weight Trends for Regional Turbo-Propeller Driven Airplanes

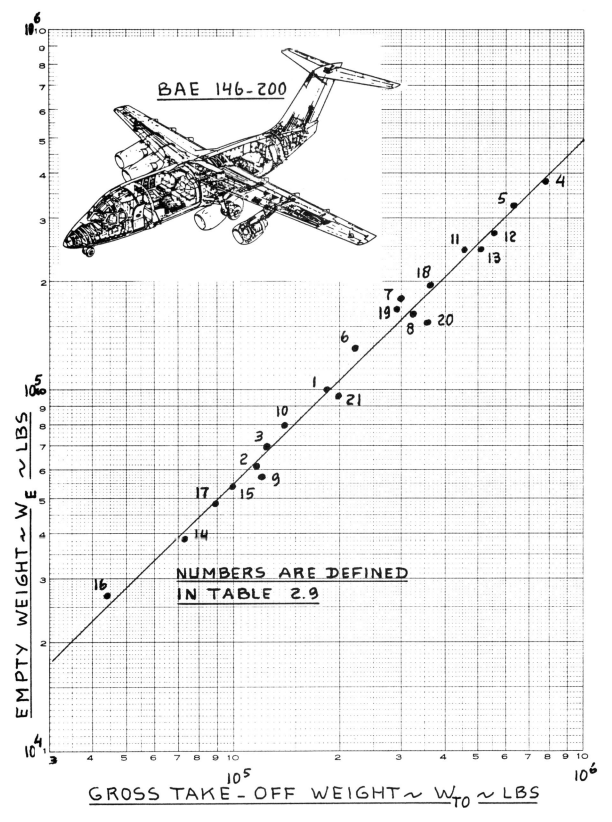

BAE 146-200

NUMBERS ARE DEFINED
IN TABLE 2.9

EMPTY WEIGHT ~ W_E ~ LBS

GROSS TAKE-OFF WEIGHT ~ W_{TO} ~ LBS

Figure 2.9 Weight Trends for Transport Jets

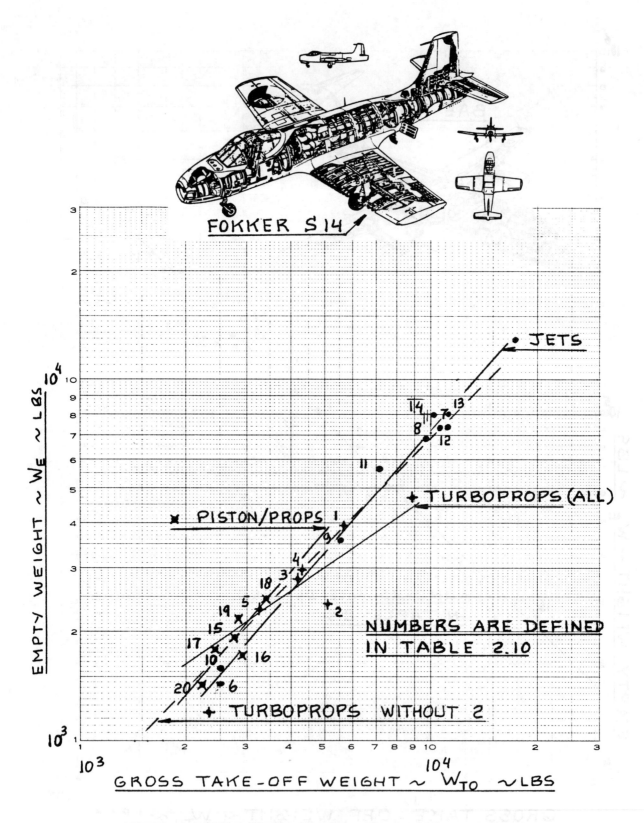

FOKKER S 14

Figure 2.10 Weight Trends for Military Trainers

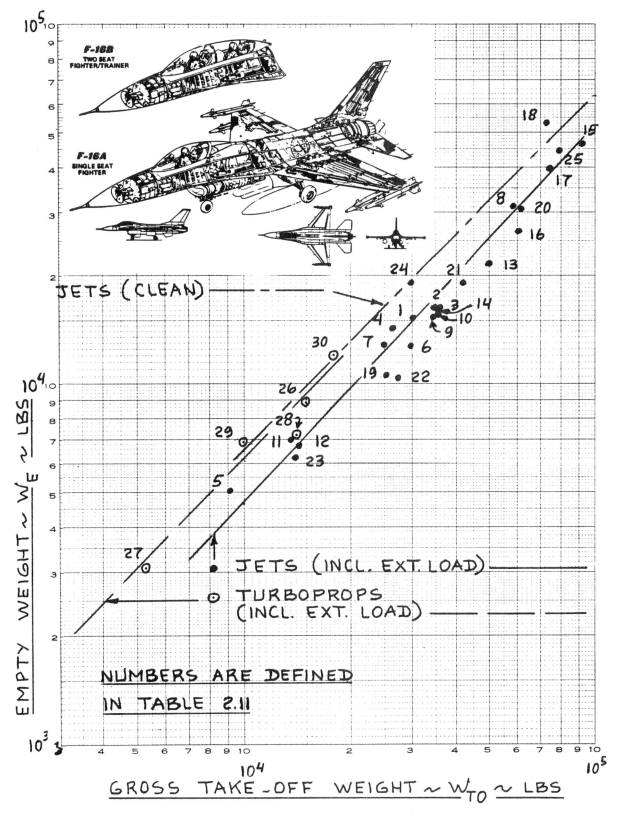

Figure 2.11 Weight Trends for Fighters

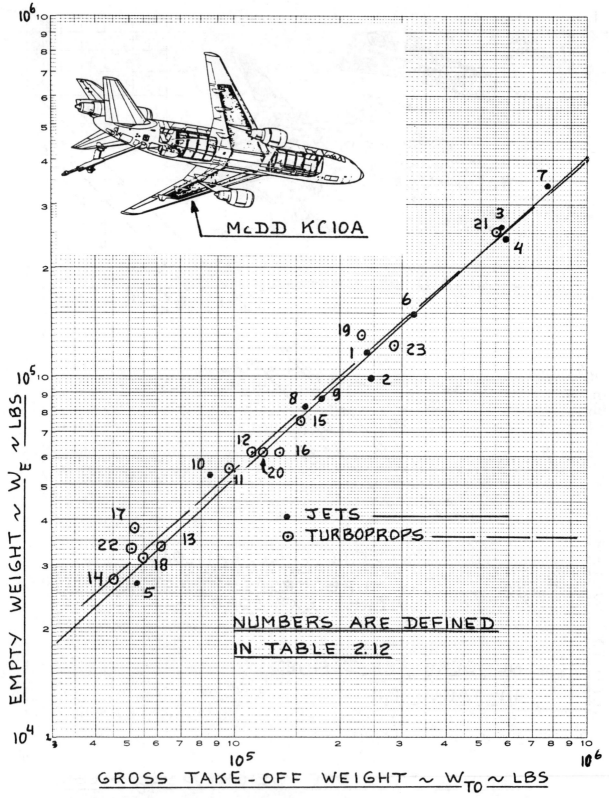

Figure 2.12 Weight Trends for Military Patrol, Bomb and
Transport Airplanes

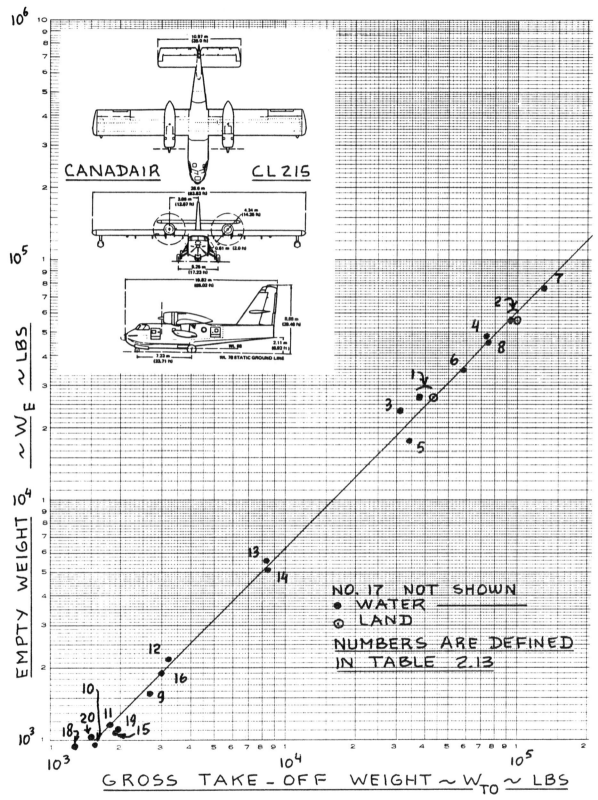

Figure 2.13 Weight Trends for Flying Boats and
Amphibious and Float Airplanes

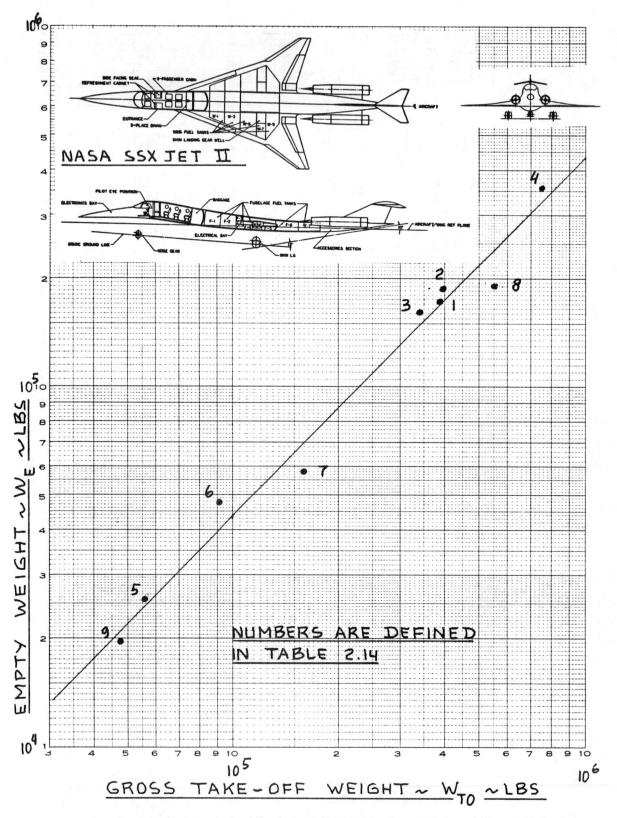

NASA SSX JET II

NUMBERS ARE DEFINED
IN TABLE 2.14

EMPTY WEIGHT ~ W_E ~ LBS

GROSS TAKE-OFF WEIGHT ~ W_{TO} ~ LBS

Figure 2.14 Weight Trends for Supersonic Cruise Airplanes

Table 2.3 Weight Data for Homebuilt Propeller Driven Airplanes
===

No.	Type	Gross Take-off Weight, W_{TO} (lbs)	Empty Weight, W_E (lbs)	Maximum Landing Weight, W_{Land} (lbs)	Max. Internal Fuel Weight, W_{MIF} (lbs)
	PERSONAL FUN OR TRANSPORTATION				
	USA				
1	Bowers Fly Baby 1-B	972	651	972	94
2	Bushby MM-1-85	875	575	875	88
3	Cassutt II	800	433	800	85
4	Monnett Sonerai I	750	440	750	59
5	Mooney Mite	780	505	780	64
6	Pazmany PL-2A	1,416	875	1,416	147
7	Pazmany PL-4A	850	578	850	70
8	Quickie Q2	1,000*	475	1,000	117
9	Rutan Variviggen	1,700*	950	1,700	205
10	Rutan Varieze	1,050*	560	1,050	141
11	Rutan Longeze	1,325*	750	1,325	305
	CANADA				
12	Zenith-CH 200	1,499	881	1,433	139
	FINLAND				
13	PIK-21	705	438	705	62
	FRANCE				
14	Croses EAC-3	573	310	573	15
15	Gatard AG02	617	375	617	46
16	Jodel D92	705	420	705	39
17	Jurca M.J.5EA2	1,499	947	1,499	180
18	Piel Emeraude CP320	1,433	903	1,433	124
19	Piel Super Diamant	1,873	1,146	1,873	248
20	Pottier P50	882	595	882	93
	ITALY				
21	Stelio Frati Falco F8L	1,808	1,212	1,808	183

*Constructed from composites

NP = nose prop
PP = pusher prop

1 pilot, NP →1
1 pilot, NP →3
1 pilot, NP →5
2 crew, PP
1 pilot, PP
1 pilot
1 pilot, NP

Table 2.3 (Cont'd) Weight Data for Homebuilt Propeller Driven Airplanes

No.	Type	Gross Take-off Weight, W_{TO} and Maximum Landing Weight, W_{Land} (lbs)	Empty Weight, W_E (lbs)	Max. Internal Fuel Weight, W_{MIF} (lbs)	Builder
	SCALED WWII FIGHTERS				
	USA				
22	2/3 Westland Whirlwind	1,400	1,042	117	Butterworth
23	7/10 Ju87B-2 Stuka	2,275	1,680	182	Langhurst
24	2/3 NAA P 51	780	460	135	Meyer
25	8/10 Spitfire IX	2,505	1,905	382	Thunder Wings
26	8/10 Curtiss P-40	3,204	2,630	264	N.A.
27	8/10 FW 190A	2,575	1,978	294	N.A.
28	1/2 F4U Corsair	1,200	921	N.A.	WAR
29	1/2 FW 190A	900	630	70	WAR
30	5/8 Hurricane IIC	1,375	1,005	176	Sindlinger
31	4/5 Boeing F4B/P12	2,100	1,530	235	Aero-Tech
	FRANCE				
32	2/3 P 51	1,875	1,485	N.A.	Jurca MJ7
33	3/4 FW 190A	1,380	880	N.A.	Jurca MJ8
	ENGLAND				
34	6/10 Spitfire	1,100	805	71	Isaacs
	CANADA				
35	3/4 Reggiane 2000 Falco 1	1,950	1,260	N.A.	Tesori

Table 2.4 Weight Data for Single Engine Propeller Driven Airplanes
===

No.	Type	Gross Take-off Weight, W_{TO} (lbs)	Empty Weight, W_E (lbs)	Maximum Landing Weight, W_{Land} (lbs)	Max. Internal Fuel Weight, W_{MIF} (lbs)
	BEECH				
1	Sierra 200	2,750	1,694	2,750	335
2	Bonanza A36	3,600	2,195	3,600	434
3	Bonanza V35B	3,400	2,106	3,400	434
4	Turbo Bonanza	3,850	2,338	3,850	599
5	Skipper 77	1,675	1,100	1,675	170
	CESSNA				
6	152	1,670	1,112	1,670	229
7	Skyhawk II	2,400	1,427	2,400	252
8	Skylane RG	3,100	1,757	3,100	517
9	Skywagon 185	3,350	1,700	3,350	517
10	Stationair 8	3,800	2,123	3,800	358
11	Centurion II	3,800	2,153	3,800	511
12	Centurion Press.	4,000	2,426	3,800	511
13	Caravan 208 (TBP)	7,750	3,385	7,000	2,194
	PIPER				
14	Warrior II	2,325	1,348	2,325	282
15	Arrow IV	2,750	1,637	2,750	452
16	Saratoga	3,600	1,935	3,600	628
17	Tripacer PA22	2,000	1,110	2,000	211
18	Super Cub PA18-150	1,750	930	1,750	211
	DeHAVILLAND				
19	DHC-2 Beaver (land)	5,100	2,850	5,100	556
20	DHC-3 Otter (land)	8,000	4,168	8,000	1,286
	SOCATA				
21	Rallye 125	1,852	1,125	1,852	149
22	Diplomate ST-10	2,690	1,594	2,690	310

Table 2.4 (Cont'd) Weight Data for Single Engine Propeller Driven Airplanes

No.	Type	Gross Take-off Weight, W_{TO} (lbs)	Empty Weight, W_E (lbs)	Maximum Landing Weight, W_{Land} (lbs)	Max. Internal Fuel Weight, W_{MIF} (lbs)
	ZLIN				
23	142	2,138	1,609	2,138	194
24	Z50L	1,587	1,256	1,587	93
	MOONEY				
25	201(M20J)	2,740	1,640	2,740	376
26	231 Turbo(M20K)	2,900	1,800	2,900	462
27	Antonov AN-2	11,574	7,275	N.A.	1,984
28	Beagle B.121-2 Pup	1,900	1,090	1,900	169
29	Partenavia P66C	2,183	1,322	2,183	251
30	Fuji FA-200	2,335	1,366	2,335	317
31	Pilatus PC-6(TBP)	4,850	2,685	4,850	832
32	Varga 2150A Kachina	1,817	1,125	1,817	205

Table 2.5 Weight Data for Twin Engine Propeller Driven Airplanes

No.	Type	Gross Take-off Weight, W_{TO} (lbs)	Empty Weight, W_E (lbs)	Maximum Landing Weight, W_{Land} (lbs)	Max. Internal Fuel Weight, W_{MIF} (lbs)	Crew/Cap
	BEECH					
1	Duchess 76	3,900	2,466	3,900	587	1/3
2	Baron 95-B55	5,100	3,236	5,100	587	1/5
3	Duke B60	6,775	4,423	6,775	834	1/5
4	King Air C90 (TBP)	9,650	5,765	9,168	2,515	2/7
	CESSNA					
5	Crusader T303	5,150	3,305	5,000	898	1/5
6	340A	5,990	3,948	5,990	1,192	1/5
7	402C Businessliner	6,850	4,077	6,850	1,250	2/8
8	414A Chancellor	6,750	4,368	6,750	1,250	2/8
9	421 Golden Eagle	7,450	4,668	7,450	1,250	2/6
10	Conquest I (TBP)	8,200	4,915	8,000	2,443	1/7
	PIPER					
11	Navajo	6,500	4,003	6,500	1,127	2/7
12	Chieftain	7,000	4,221	7,000	1,127	2/7
13	Aerostar 600A	5,500	3,737	5,500	1,018	1/5
14	Seminole PA-44-180	3,800	2,354	3,800	646	1/3
15	Seminole PA-44-180T	3,800	2,430	3,800	646	1/3
16	Cheyenne I (TBP)	8,700	4,910	8,700	2,017	1/6
17	Wing Derringer D-1	3,050	2,100	2,900	511	2/0
18	Partenavia P66C-160	2,183	1,322	2,183	251	2/2
19	Piaggio P166-DL3 (TBP)	9,480	5,732	8,377	1,850	2/8-10
20	Gulf-Am 840A (TBP)	10,325	6,629	10,325	2,784	2/6
21	Learfan 2100 (TBP)	7,350*	4,100	7,000	1,572	2/6
22	Rutan 40 Defiant	2,900*	1,610	2,900	528	1/3

* 21 and 22 are composite built airplanes

Table 2.6 Weight Data for Agricultural Airplanes
===

No.	Type	Gross Take-off Weight, W_{TO} (lbs)	Empty Weight, W_E(lbs)	Maximum Landing Weight, W_{Land} (lbs)	Max. Internal Fuel Weight, W_{MIF}(lbs)
	PISTON-PROPS				
1	EMB-201A (N)	3,417	2,229	3,417	1,714
2	PZL-104	2,866	1,880	2,866	1,145
3	PZL-106	6,614	3,550	6,614	1,761
4	PZL-M18A	9,259	5,445	9,259	2,348
5	Transavia T-300	4,244	2,242	3,800	293
6	Ayres S2R-R1820	10,000	4,990	N.A.	1,115
7	Schweizer AG-CATB	7,020	3,525	7,020 470	
8	Cessna AG Husky*	3,500	2,306	3,300	317
9	Cessna AG Truck	3,300	2,229	3,300	317
10	Piper PA-36 Brave	3,900	2,050	3,900	528
11	IAR-827A	6,173	3,660	N.A.	713
	TURBO-PROPS				
12	Pilatus PC-6	6,100	2,995	4,850	837
13	NDN 6	10,000	4,500	N.A.	1,524
14	Ayres Turbo-Thrush	6,000	3,900	N.A.	1,245
15	Air Tractor AT400	6,000	3,550	N.A.	825
16	Marsh S2R-T	6,000	3,600	N.A.	694
	JETS				
17	PZL M-15	12,675	7,120	8,815	2,525

* Turbocharged
Note: Weights listed are for the 'normal category'.

TURBOFANS

Table 2.7 Weight Data for Business Jets
===

No.	Type	Gross Take-off Weight, W_{TO} (lbs)	Empty Weight, W_E (lbs)	Maximum Landing Weight, W_{Land} (lbs)	Max. Internal Fuel Weight, W_{MIF} (lbs)
1	Canadair Cl-601	41,650	19,960	36,000	16,725
	DASSAULT-BREGUET				
2	Falcon 20F	28,660	16,600	19,685	9,170
3	Falcon 10	18,740	10,760	17,640	5,910
4	Falcon 50	38,800	19,840	35,715	15,520
5	IAI Westwind 2	22,850	12,300	19,000	8,515
6	BAe-700	25,500	12,845	22,000	9,288
	CESSNA				
7	Citation I	11,850	6,605	11,350	3,780
8	Citation II	13,300	7,196	12,700	5,009
9	Citation III	20,000	10,951	16,500	7,155
	GATES LEARJET				
10	Learjet 55	19,500	12,130	17,000	6,707
11	Learjet 24	13,500	7,064	11,880	5,628
12	Learjet 25	15,000	7,650	13,300	6,098
13	Gulfstream IIB	68,200	38,750	58,500	28,300
14	Lockheed Jetstar	43,750	23,828	36,000	14,253
15	Mitsub. Diamond I	14,630	9,100	13,200	4,260
16	Rockw. Sabrel. 65	24,000	13,400	21,755	8,626
17	Foxjet(not built)	4,550	2,408	N.A.	N.A.
18	Piaggio PD-808	18,000	10,650	16,000	6,445
19	HFB320 Hansa	20,280	11,775	19,400	6,084

Cup/Crew/Eng

2/19/2 1
2/14/2 2
2/9/3   3 4
2/10/2 5
2/5/2   7
2/8/2   8
2/11/2 9
2/10/2 10
2/6/2   11
2/12/2 12
2/19/2 13
3/10/4 14
5/7/2   16

Table 2.8 Weight Data for Regional Turbo-Propeller Driven Airplanes

No.	Type	Gross Take-off Weight, W_{TO} (lbs)	Empty Weight, W_E (lbs)	Maximum Landing Weight, W_{Land} (lbs)	Max. Internal Fuel Weight, W_{MIF} (lbs)
1	Antonov 28	14,330	7,716	14,330	3,483
2	Casa C212-200	16,424	9,072	16,204	3,527
3	BAe 748 2B(A)	46,500	26,560	43,000	11,326
4	Shorts 330	22,900	14,175	22,600	3,840
5	Shorts 360	25,700	16,075	25,400	3,840
6	Shorts SC7-3	12,500	7,750	12,500	2,303
7	Beech 1900	15,245	8,500	15,245	2,855
8	Beech C99	11,300	6,494	11,300	2,466
9	Beech King Air B200	12,500	7,538	12,500	3,645
10	Cessna Conquest I	8,200	4,915	8,000	2,459
11	Cessna Conquest II	9,850	5,682	9,360	3,183
12	FS Metro III	14,500	8,387	14,000	4,342
13	Gulfstream IC	36,000	23,693	34,285	10,460
14	GAF Nomad N22B	8,500	4,613	8,500	1,770
15	Fokker F27 Mk200	45,000	25,525	41,000	9,090
16	ATR-42-200	34,720	20,580	33,730	9,920
17	Aeritalia AP68TP-200	5,732	3,245	5,445	1,340
18	SM SF600 Canguro	7,054	4,299	7,054	1,902
19	Airtec CN235	28,660	16,094	28,220	8,818
20	DeHavilland DHC-7	44,000	27,000	42,000	9,925
21	DeHavilland DHC-5D Buffalo (A)	41,000	24,635	39,100	13,696
22	EMB-120 Brasilia	21,165	11,945	21,165	5,624
23	Saab-Fairchild 340	26,000	15,510	25,500	5,900
24	Piper PA-31T Cheyenne II	9,000	5,018	9,000	2,555

Handwritten annotations (Crew/Cap/Eng):
2/8/2, 2/26/2, 3/30/2, 3/36/2, 2/19/2, 1/15/2, 1/7/2, 2/16/2, 2/24/2, 3/56/2, 3/50/2, 1/6/2, 2/9/2, 3/44/2, 3/50/4, 3/41/2, 3/37/2, 2/6/2

Table 2.8 (Cont'd) Weight Data for Regional Turbo-Propeller Driven Airplanes

No.	Type	Gross Take-off Weight, W_{TO} (lbs)	Empty Weight W_E (lbs)	Maximum Landing Weight, W_{Land} (lbs)	Max. Internal Fuel Weight, W_{MIF} (lbs)
25	Piper PA-42 Cheyenne III	11,200	6,389	10,330	2,686
26	BAe 31 Jetstream	14,550	7,606	14,550	3,017
27	Embraer EMB-110 Bandeirante	12,500	7,837	12,500	2,974
28	DeHavilland DHC-6 Twin Otter-300	12,500	7,065	12,500	2,500
29	DeHavilland DHC-8	30,500	20,176	30,000	5,875
30	Dornier 128-6	9,590	5,230	9,127	1,544
31	Dornier 228-200	12,566	6,495	See '84 Janes	See '84 Janes
32	Arava 202	15,000	8,816	15,000	2,876
33	DeHavilland DHC-7, Series 300	57,250	34,250	55,600	10,000

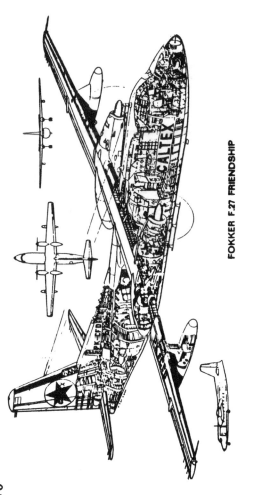

FOKKER F.27 FRIENDSHIP

Table 2.9 Weight Data for Transport Jets
==

No.	Type	Gross Take-off Weight, W_{TO} (lbs)	Empty Weight*, W_E (lbs)	Maximum Landing Weight, W_{Land} (lbs)	Max. Internal Fuel Weight, W_{MIF} (lbs)	Cap/Eng
	BOEING					
1	727-200	184,800	100,000	154,500	52,990	151/3
2	737-200	115,500	61,630	103,000	39,104	136/2
3	737-300	124,500	69,930	114,000	35,108	149/2
4	747-200B	775,000	380,000	564,000	343,279	366/4
5	747-SP	630,000	325,000	450,000	329,851	331/4
6	757-200	220,000	130,420	198,000	73,229	239/2
7	767-200	300,000	179,082	270,000	109,385	255-200/2
	McDONNELL-DOUGLAS					
8	DC8-Super 71	325,000	162,700	240,000	156,733	200-250/4
9	DC9-30	121,000	57,190	110,000	24,117	115/2
10	DC9-80	140,000	79,757	128,000	37,852	175/2
11	DC10-10	455,000	244,903	363,500	142,135	399/3
12	DC10-40	555,000	271,062	403,000	239,075	399/3
13	Lockheed L1011-500	510,000	245,500	368,000	155,982	246/3
14	Fokker F28-4000	73,000	38,683	69,500	16,842	85/2
15	Rombac-111-560	99,650	53,762	87,000	24,549	119/2
16	VFW-Fokker 614	44,000	26,850	44,000	10,928	44/2
17	BAe 146-200	89,500	48,500	77,500	22,324	112/4
	AIRBUS					
18	A300-B4-200	363,760	195,109	295,420	195,109	266/2
19	A310-202	291,000	168,910	261,250	94,798	200/2
20	Ilyushin-Il-62M	357,150	153,000	231,500	183,700	108-186/4
21	Tupolev-154	198,416	95,900	176,370	73,085	114-170/3

* W_E here means typical airline operating weight empty, W_{OE}

Table 2.10 Weight Data for Military Trainers

No.	Type	Gross Take-off Weight, W_{TO} (lbs)	Empty Weight, W_E (lbs)	Maximum Landing Weight, W_{Land} (lbs)	Max. Internal Fuel Weight, W_{MIF} (lbs)
	TURBO-PROPS				
1	EMB-312 Tucano	5,622	3,946	6,173	1,193
2	RFB Fantrainer 600B	5,070	2,337	4,409	750
3	Pilatus PC7/CH	4,188	2,800	4,188	820
4	Beech T34C	4,300	2,960	4,300	852
5	NDN1T Firecracker	3,250	2,300	3,250	738
	JETS				
6	Microjet 200	2,535	1,433	2,491	688
7	MDB Alpha Jet	11,023	7,374	11,023	3,351
8	MB339A	9,700	6,889	N.A.	2,425
9	SM S211	5,511	3,560	5,511	2,491
10	Caproni C22J	2,502	1,587	2,502	540
11	PZL TS-11	7,150	5,644	7,150	2,421
12	CASA C-101	10,692	7,385	10,361	4,078
13	BAe Hawk Mk1	11,100	8,040	10,250	2,497
14	Aero Albatros L39	10,028	7,859	9,480	2,170
	PISTON-PROPS				
15	Aerosp. Epsilon	2,755	1,936	2,755	325
16	Chincul Arrow	2,900	1,730	2,900	421
17	SM-SF260M	2,425	1,797	2,425	377
18	Fuji KM-2B T-3	3,400	2,469	3,329	411
19	Yakovlev-52	2,844	2,205	2,844	189
20	BAe Bulldog 121	2,233	1,430	2,238	226

Note: Weights listed are for the airplanes in a clean configuration. With external loads most weights will increase significantly.

Table 2.11 Weight Data for Fighters
===

No.	Type	Gross Take-off Weight, W_{TO} (lbs)		Empty Weight, W_E (lbs)	Maximum Landing Weight, W_{Land} (lbs)	Max. Internal Fuel Weight, W_{MIF} (lbs)
		CLEAN	WITH EXT. LOAD			
	JETS					
1	MD Mirage III	21,165	30,200	15,540	N.A.	5,188
2	MD Mirage F-1	24,030	35,715	16,314	N.A.	5,188
3	MD Mirage 2000N	N.A.	36,375	16,315	N.A.	6,571
4	MD Etendard*	20,833	26,455	14,330	N.A.	5,654
5	HAL Ajeet**	7,803	9,200	5,086	6,100	2,334
6	McDD AV8B**	N.A.	29,750	12,750	19,400	7,500
7	BAe Harrier**	N.A.	25,000	12,800	N.A.	4,954
8	Tornado F.Mk2	45,000	58,400	31,065	N.A.	N.A.
9	Sepecat Jaguar	24,149	34,612	15,432	N.A.	7,263
10	IAI Kfir	20,700	35,715	16,060	N.A.	5,670
11	MB339 Veltro 2	10,974	13,558	6,997	N.A.	3,487
12	SAAB 105G	10,714	14,330	6,757	N.A.	3,458
13	F.R. A10A	32,771	50,000	21,541	N.A.	10,700
14	G.D. F16A	23,810	35,400	15,586	N.A.	6,972
15	G.D. F111A*	N.A.	91,500	46,172	N.A.	N.A.
16	Grumman A6*	N.A.	60,400	26,660	45,000	15,939
17	Grumman F14A*	N.A.	74,348	39,762	51,830	16,200
18	Grumman EF111A	N.A.	72,750	53,418	80,000	32,894
19	Northrop F5F	N.A.	25,225	10,567	25,147	4,434
20	McDD F4E	N.A.	61,795	30,328	46,000	12,150
21	Vought A7E	N.A.	42,000	19,111	N.A.	9,825

* Carrier suitable fighter. ** V/STOL fighter.

Table 2.11 (Cont'd) Weight Data for Fighters

No.	Type	Gross Take-off Weight, W_{TO} (lbs) CLEAN	Gross Take-off Weight, W_{TO} (lbs) WITH EXT. LOAD	Empty Weight, W_E (lbs)	Maximum Landing Weight, W_{Land} (lbs)	Max. Internal Fuel Weight, W_{MIF} (lbs)
	JETS					
22	McDD A4F	N.A.	27,420	10,448	N.A.	11,790
23	Cessna A37B	N.A.	14,000	6,211	14,000	3,321
24	Sukhoi Su 7BM	N.A.	29,750	19,000	N.A.	7,000
25	MiG 25A	N.A.	79,800	44,100	N.A.	30,865
	TURBOPROPS					
26	FMA IA58B Pucara	N.A.	14,991	8,884	12,345	2,215
27	GA F20TP Condor	N.A.	5,291	3,086	5,291	1,038
28	Piper PA-48 Enforcer		14,000	7,200	8,000	2,777
29	Rockwell OV10A	N.A.	9,908	6,893	N.A.	1,651
30	Grumman OV-1D Mohawk	N.A.	17,912	12,054	N.A.	1,808

PANAVIA 200 MRCA

Table 2.12 Weight Data for Military Patrol, Bomb and Transport Airplanes
===

No.	Type	Gross Take-off Weight, W_{TO} (lbs)	Empty Weight, W_E (lbs)	Maximum Landing Weight, W_{Land} (lbs)	Max. Internal Fuel Weight, W_{MIF} (lbs)
	JETS				
1	Boeing YC-14 **	237,000	117,500	N.A.	66,400
2	Boeing KC-135A	245,000	98,466	185,000	N.A.
3	McDD C17	572,000	259,000	N.A.	N.A.
4	McDD KC-10A	590,000	240,065	403,000	228,975
5	Lockheed S3A	52,539 ***	26,650 *	45,914	12,445
6	Lockheed C141B	323,100	148,120 *	343,000	154,527
7	Lockheed C5A	769,000	337,937	635,850	320,950
8	Tupolev Tu-16	158,730	82,000	N.A.	78,592
9	BAe Nimrod Mk2	177,500	86,000	120,000	84,350
10	NAMC XC-1	85,320	53,130	N.A.	26,284
	TURBOPROPS				
11	DB Atlantic-II	96,780	55,775	79,365	40,785
12	Transall C-160	112,435	61,730	103,615	38,480
13	Aeritalia G222	61,730	33,950	58,420	20,725
14	Fokker F27 Maritime	45,000	27,600 *	41,000	16,000
15	Lockheed C130E	155,000	75,331	130,000	63,404
16	Lockheed P3C	135,000	61,491	103,880	60,260
17	Grumman E2C	51,817	37,945	N.A.	12,400
18	Grumman C2A	54,830	31,154	47,372	11,947
19	Shorts Belfast	230,000	130,000	215,000	82,400
20	Antonov AN12	121,475	61,730	N.A.	31,299
21	Antonov AN22	551,160	251,325	N.A.	94,800
22	Antonov AN26	50,706	33,113	50,706	12,125
23	Douglas C133B	286,000	120,363	N.A.	118,634

* These weights are typical W_{OE} values. ** This is a STOL airplane.
*** for 2.50g only. W_{TO} = 343,000 lbs for 2.25g.

Handwritten marginal notes:

HW = high wing
LW = low wing
T = transport B = bomber
P = patrol

wing/eng:
1 HW/2 T
2 LW/4 T
3 HW/4 T
4 LW/3 T
5 LW/2 B
6 HW/4 T
7 HW/4 T
8 MW/2 B
9 LW/4 P
10 HW/2 T
LW/4 → (15/16) P (16)

Table 2.13 Weight Data for Flying Boats and Amphibious and Float Airplanes
==

No.	Type	Gross Take-off Weight, W_{TO} (lbs)	Empty Weight, W_E (lbs)	Maximum Landing Weight, W_{Land} (lbs)	Max. Internal Fuel Weight, W_{MIF} (lbs)
1	Canadair CL-215	43,500(L) 37,700(W)	26,810 26,810	34,400(L) 37,000(W)	9,159 9,159
2	Shin Meiwa US-1(TBP)	99,200(L) 94,800(W)	56,218 56,218	N.A. N.A.	38,620 38,620
3	Grumman Albatros	30,800(L) 31,150(W)	23,500 23,500	29,160(L) 31,150(W)	6,438 6,438
4	Martin P5M2	74,000	48,000	N.A.	23,333
5	Consol.V PBY-5	34,000	17,564	N.A.	10,273
	SHORTS				
6	Sunderland III	58,000	34,500	N.A.	15,540
7	Shetland	130,000	74,985	N.A.	45,000
8	Seaford	75,000	45,000	N.A.	N.A.
9	Lake 200 Buccaneer	2,690	1,555	2,690	323
10	Osprey II	1,560	970	1,560	153
11	Spencer Air Car Jr	1,800	1,150	1,800	317
12	Spencer Air Car Sr	3,200	2,190	3,200	552
13	GAF N22B(Amph)(TBP)	8,300	5,560	N.A.	1,770
14	GAF N22B(Float)(TBP)	8,500	5,050	N.A.	1,770
15	AAC S1B2(Float)	1,900	1,073	1,900	235
16	IAC TA16	3,000	1,900	3,000	540
17	Militi MB3 Leonardo	683	452	683	N.A.
18	Mukai Olive SM6 III	1,268	948	1,268	46
19	Aerocar Sooper-Coot	1,950	1,100	1,950	294
20	Anderson Kingfisher	1,500	1,032	1,500	117

Notes: 1. (L) indicates Land, (W) indicates Water.
2. (Float) indicates a float equipped airplane.
3. (Amph) indicates an amphibious airplane, (TBP) indicates turboprop.
All others are Piston-Propeller equipped.

Table 2.14 Weight Data for Supersonic Cruise Airplanes
==

No.	Type	Gross Take-off Weight, W_{TO} (lbs)	Empty Weight, W_E (lbs)	Maximum Landing Weight, W_{Land} (lbs)	Max. Internal Fuel Weight, W_{MIF} (lbs)
1	Concorde	389,000	172,000*	245,000	202,809
2	TU144	396,830	187,400*	264,500	209,440
3	Boeing 969-512BA	340,194	162,510	N.A.	155,501
4	Boeing 969-512BB	750,000	358,270	N.A.	342,824
5	SM-SST	56,200	25,200	45,000	29,800
6	GD-F111A	91,500	47,500	N.A.	N.A.
7	GD-B58A	160,000	58,000	N.A.	98,250
8	NAA B70A	550,000	190,000	N.A.	300,000
9	NASA Supersonic Cruise Fighter (n=4)	47,900	19,620	N.A.	N.A.
10	Rockwell B1B	477,000	N.A.	422,000	N.A.

Notes:
1. Airplanes 1 through 5 are commercial transports.
2. Airplanes 3 through 5 are study projects only.
3. Remaining airplanes are military.
* Indicates W_{OE} in these cases.

ROCKWELL B1B

Table 2.15 Regression Line Constants A and B of Equation (2.16)
==

Airplane Type	A	B
1. Homebuilts		
Pers. fun and transportation	0.3411	0.9519
Scaled Fighters	0.5542	0.8654
Composites	0.8222	0.8050
2. Single Engine Propeller Driven	-0.1440	1.1162
3. Twin Engine Propeller Driven	0.0966	1.0298
Composites	0.1130	1.0403
4. Agricultural	-0.4398	1.1946
5. Business Jets	0.2678	0.9979
6. Regional TBP	0.3774	0.9647
7. Transport Jets	0.0833	1.0383

Airplane Type	A	B
8. Military Trainers		
Jets	0.6632	0.8640
Turboprops	-1.4041	1.4660
Turboprops without No.2	0.1677	0.9978
Piston/Props	0.5627	0.8761
9. Fighters		
Jets(+ ext.load)	0.5091	0.9505
Jets(clean)	0.1362	1.0116
Turboprops(+ ext.load)	0.2705	0.9830
10. Mil. Patrol, Bomb and Transport		
Jets	-0.2009	1.1037
Turboprops	-0.4179	1.1446
11. Flying Boats, Amphibious and Float Airplanes	0.1703	1.0083
12. Supersonic Cruise	0.4221	0.9876

Equation (2.16) is repeated here for convenience:

$$W_E = invlog_{10}\{(log_{10}W_{TO} - A)/B\}$$

Table 2.16 Weight Reduction Data for Use of New Materials
==
in Primary and Secondary Airplane Structures
===

Structural Component:	W_{new}/W_{old} when made of:		
	Composites	ARALL	Al-Li
Primary Structure			
Fuselage	0.75 – 0.85	0.75	0.90
Wing, Vertical Tail, Canard or Horizontal Tail	0.75	0.75	0.90
Landing Gear	0.88	N.A.	0.90
Secondary Structure			
Flaps, Slats, Access Panels, Fairings	0.70	0.80	0.90
Interior Furnishings	0.50 – 0.70	N.A.	N.A.
Air Induction System	0.70 – 0.80	0.75	0.90

IMPORTANT NOTES:

1) These weight reduction factors should be used with due caution! They are valid only when changing from 100% conventional aluminum alloys to 100% new materials.

2) The composite weight reduction numbers are applicable to certain military airplanes and to homebuilt airplanes. For FAR 23 and FAR 25 certified airplanes the composite numbers are not attainable due to lightning strike and hail strike certification requirements. The ARALL and Al-Li numbers do apply in these cases!!

3) The reader should also refer to Appendix B.

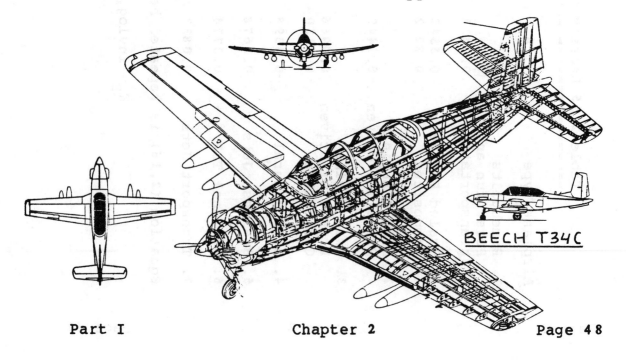

BEECH T34C

2.6 THREE EXAMPLE APPLICATIONS

The method for estimating W_{TO}, W_E and W_F will now be illustrated with three examples:

    2.6.1 Example 1: Twin Engine Propeller Driven Propeller Driven Airplane
    2.6.2 Example 2: Jet Transport
    2.6.3 Example 3: Fighter

2.6.1 Example 1: Twin Engine Propeller Driven Airplane

Table 2.17 gives an example mission specification for a twin engine propeller driven airplane. Note that the various mission phases have been numbered. The example follows the step-by-step procedure outlined in Section 2.1.

Step 1. From Table 2.17, the payload weight, W_{PL} is:

$$W_{PL} = 6 \times 175 + 200 = 1,250 \text{ lbs}$$

Step 2. A likely value for W_{TO} is obtained by looking at data for similar airplanes. In Reference 9, the following information can be found:

Airplane Type	W_{PL} (lbs)	W_{TO} (lbs)	$V_{cr_{max}}$ (kts)	Range (nm)
Beech Duke B60	1,300	6,775	239	1,080
Beech Baron M58	1,500	5,400	200	1,200
Cessna T303	1,650	5,150	196	1,000
Piper PA-44-180	1,250	3,800	168	725

From these data a value for W_{TO} of 7,000 lbs seems reasonable, so:

$$W_{TO_{guess}} = 7,000 \text{ lbs}$$

Step 3. To determine a value for W_F, the procedure indicated in Section 2.4 will be followed. Mission phases are defined in Table 2.17.

Table 2.17 Mission Specification For A Twin Engine

===

Propeller Driven Airplane

===========================

Payload: Six passengers at 175 lbs each (this
                      includes the pilot) and 200 lbs total
                      baggage.

Range: 1,000 sm with max. payload. Reserves
                      equal to 25% of required mission fuel.

Altitude: 10,000 ft (for the design range).

Cruise Speed: 250 kts at 75% power at 10,000 ft.

Climb: 10 minutes to 10,000 feet at max. W_{TO}.

Take-off and

Landing: 1,500 ft groundrun at sealevel, std. day.
                      Landing performance at $W_L = 0.95W_{TO}$.

Powerplants: Piston/Propeller

Pressurization: None

Certification
Base: FAR 23

Mission Profile:

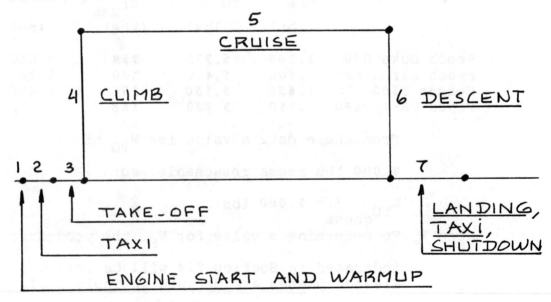

Phase 1: Engine start and warm-up.
Begin weight is W_{TO}. End weight is W_1.

The ratio W_1/W_{TO} is typically 0.992 as indicated in Table 2.1.

Phase 2: Taxi.
Begin weight is W_1. End weight is W_2.

The ratio W_2/W_1 is typically 0.996 as indicated in Table 2.1.

Phase 3: Take-off.
Begin weight is W_2. End weight is W_3.

The ratio W_3/W_2 is typically 0.996 as indicated in Table 2.1.

Phase 4: Climb to cruise altitude.
Begin weight is W_3. End weight is W_4.

The ratio W_4/W_3 depends on the climb

performance of the airplane which is being designed and on the specified cruise altitude. A reasonable value for this ratio is 0.990 as indicated in Table 2.1.

Phase 5: Cruise.
Begin weight is W_4. End weight is W_5.

The ratio W_5/W_4 can be estimated from

Breguet's range equation which for propeller-driven airplanes is:

$$R_{cr} = 375(\eta_p/c_p)_{cr}(L/D)_{cr}\ln(W_4/W_5) \qquad (2.9)$$

From Table 2.17 the range, R is 1,000 sm.

During cruise, $c_p = 0.5$ lbs/hp/hr and

$\eta_p = 0.82$ are reasonable choices,

according to Table 2.2. With good aero-dynamic design a value of L/D=11 should be attainable, even though Table 2.2

suggests that a value of 10 is high.
With these numbers, Eqn.(2.9) yields:

$$1,000 = 375(0.82/0.5)(11)\ln(W_4/W_5)$$

from which is found:

$$W_5/W_4 = 0.863.$$

Phase 6: Descent.
Begin weight is W_5. End weight is W_6.

The fuel-fraction follows from Table 2.1:

$$W_6/W_5 = 0.992.$$

Phase 7: Landing, Taxi, Shutdown.
Begin weight is W_6. End weight is W_7.

The ratio W_7/W_6 is assumed to be 0.992,

based again on Table 2.1.

The overall mission fuel fraction, M_{ff} can be
computed with the help of Eqn.(2.13):

$$M_{ff} = \left\{ \frac{W_7 W_6 W_5 W_4 W_3 W_2 W_1}{W_6 W_5 W_4 W_3 W_2 W_1 W_{TO}} \right\} =$$

$$= (0.992)(0.992)(0.863)(0.990)(0.996)(0.996)x$$
$$x(0.992) = 0.827$$

The fuel used during phases 1 through 7 is given
by Eqn.(2.14). This yields here:

$$W_{F_{used}} = (1 - 0.827)W_{TO} = 0.173W_{TO}.$$

The value for W_F needed for the mission is equal

to the fuel used plus fuel reserves. The latter
are defined in Table 2.17 as 25% of the fuel used.
Thus:

$$W_F = 0.173 x 1.25 x W_{TO} = 0.216W_{TO}$$

Step 4. A tentative value for W_{OE} is found from
Eqn.(2.4) as:

$$W_{OE_{tent}} = 7,000 - 0.216 \times 7,000 - 1,250 =$$
$$= 4,238 \text{ lbs}$$

Step 5. A tentative value for W_E is found from Eqn.(2.5) as:

$$W_{E_{tent}} = 4,238 - 0.005 \times 7,000 = 4,203 \text{ lbs.}$$
The crew is counted here as part of the payload.

Step 6. The allowable value for W_E is found from

Figure 2.5 as: $W_E = 4,300$ lbs.

Step 7. The difference between W_E and $W_{E_{tent}}$

is 97 lbs. This difference is too large. An iteration will therefore be necessary. The reader is asked to show, that when $W_{TO} = 7,900$ lbs, the following values for

empty weight are obtained:

$$W_{E_{tent}} = 4,904 \text{ lbs and:}$$
$W_E = 4,900$ lbs. These numbers are within

0.5% of each other.

To summarize, the following preliminary numbers define the airplane with the mission specification of Table 2.17:

$W_{TO} = 7,900$ lbs,

$W_E = 4,900$ lbs,

$W_F = 1,706$ lbs.

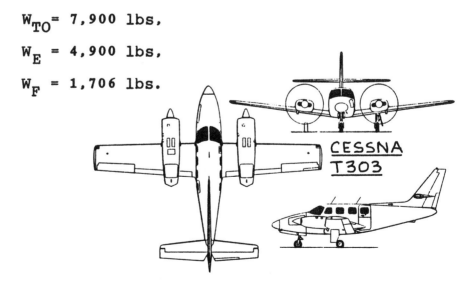

CESSNA
T303

2.6.2 Example 2: Jet Transport

Table 2.18 gives an example mission specification for a jet transport. Note that the various mission phases have been numbered. The example follows the step-by-step procedure outlined in Section 2.1.

Step 1. From Table 2.18, the payload weight, W_{PL} is:

$$W_{PL} = 150 \times (175 + 30) = 30,750 \text{ lbs}$$

Step 2. A likely value for W_{TO} is obtained by

examining data for similar airplanes. In Reference 9, the following information can be found:

Airplane Type	W_{PL} (lbs)	W_{TO} (lbs)	$V_{cr_{max}}$ (kts)	Range (nm)
Boeing 737-300	35,000	135,000	460	1,620
McDD DC9-80	38,000	140,000	M=.8	2,000
Airbus A320	42,000	145,000	450	2,700

From these data a value for W_{TO} of

130,000 lbs seems reasonable, so:

$$W_{TO_{guess}} = 130,000 \text{ lbs.}$$

Step 3. To determine a value for W_F, the procedure

indicated in Section 2.4 will be followed. Mission phases are defined in Table 2.18.

Phase 1: Engine Start and Warmup.
Begin weight is W_{TO}. End weight is W_1.

The ratio W_1/W_{TO} is typically 0.990 as

indicated in Table 2.1.

Phase 2: Taxi.
Begin weight is W_1. End weight is W_2.

The ratio W_2/W_1 is typically 0.990 as

indicated in Table 2.1.

Table 2.18 Mission Specification For A Jet Transport
==

Payload:	150 Passengers at 175 lbs each and 30 lbs of baggage each.
Crew:	Two pilots and three cabin attendants at 175 lbs each and 30 lbs baggage each.
Range:	1,500 nm, followed by 1 hour loiter, followed by a 100 nm flight to alternate.
Altitude:	35,000 ft (for the design range).
Cruise Speed:	M = 0.82 at 35,000 ft.
Climb:	Direct climb to 35,000 ft. at max. W_{TO} is desired.
Take-off and Landing:	FAR 25 fieldlength, 5,000 ft. at an altitude of 5,000 ft and a 95°F day. Landing performance at $W_L = 0.85 W_{TO}$.
Powerplants:	Two turbofans.
Pressurization:	5,000 ft. cabin at 35,000 ft.
Certification Base:	FAR 25

Mission Profile:

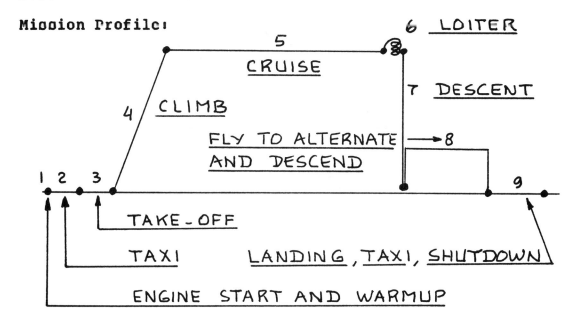

Phase 3: Take-off.
Begin weight is W_2. End weight is W_3.

The ratio W_3/W_2 is typically 0.995 as indicated by Table 2.1.

Phase 4: Climb to cruise altitude and accelerate to cruise speed.
Begin weight is W_3. End weight is W_4.

The ratio W_4/W_3 is typically 0.980 as indicated by Table 2.1.
As suggested by the mission profile of Table 2.18, range credit is to be taken for the climb. It will be assumed, that climb is performed at an average speed of 275 kts and with an average climb-rate of 2500 fpm. To 35,000 ft, it takes 14 min. and this covers a range of (14/60)x275 = 64 nm.

Phase 5: Cruise.
Begin weight is W_4. End weight is W_5.

The specification of Table 2.18 calls for a cruise Mach number of 0.82 at an altitude of 35,000 ft. This amounts to a cruise speed of 473 kts.
The amount of fuel used during cruise can be found from Breguet's range equation which for jet transports is:

$$R_{cr} = (V/c_j)_{cr} (L/D)_{cr} \ln(W_4/W_5) \qquad (2.10)$$

It will be assumed, that the transport will be able to cruise at a L/D value of 16 and an (optimistic) value of $c_j = 0.5$ lbs/lbs/hr. Table 2.2 shows these numbers to be reasonable.
Substitution of these numbers in Eqn.(2.10) with a range of 1,500 - 64 = 1436 nm, yields:

$$W_5/W_4 = 0.909$$

Phase 6: Loiter.
Begin weight is W_5. End weight is W_6.

The ratio W_6/W_5 can be estimated from

Breguet's endurance equation which for a jet transport is:

$$E_{ltr} = (1/c_j)_{ltr}(L/D)_{ltr}\ln(W_5/W_6) \qquad (2.12)$$

It will be assumed, that the transport be able to loiter at a L/D value of 18 and a value of c_j = 0.6 lbs/lbs/hr.

Table 2.2 shows these to be reasonable numbers. Note from Table 2.18, that the mission profile assumes no range credit during loiter. Loiter time is 1 hour. Substitution of the afore mentioned numbers into Eqn.(12) yields:

W_6/W_5 = 0.967.

Phase 7: Descent.
Begin weight is W_6. End weight is W_7.

No credit is taken for range. However, a penalty for fuel used during descents from high altitudes needs to be assessed. Typically the ratio W_7/W_6 = 0.990, as

seen from Table 2.1.

Phase 8: Fly to alternate and descend.
Begin weight is W_7. End weight is W_8.

The ratio W_8/W_7 can be estimated from

Eqn.(2.10). This time however, because of the short distance to fly, it will not be possible to reach an economical cruise altitude. It will be assumed, that for the cruise to alternate a value for L/D of only 10 can be achieved. For c_j a value

of only 0.9 will be used. Because the flight to alternate will probably be carried out at or below 10,000 ft, the cruise speed can be no more than 250 kts in accordance with FAA regulations. With these data and with Eqn.(2.10) it is found that:

$$W_8/W_7 = 0.965.$$

No credit or penalty was taken for the descent into the alternate airport.

Phase 9: Landing, Taxi, Shutdown.
Begin weight is W_8. End weight is W_9.

For a jet transport the ratio W_9/W_8

can be assumed to be 0.992, in accordance with Table 2.1.

The overall mission fuel-fraction, M_{ff} can now be computed from Eqn.(2.13) as:

$$M_{ff} = \left\{ \frac{W_9 W_8 W_7 W_6 W_5 W_4 W_3 W_2 W_1}{W_8 W_7 W_6 W_5 W_4 W_3 W_2 W_1 W_{TO}} \right\} =$$

$$= (0.992)(0.965)(0.990)(0.967)(0.909)(0.980) \times$$
$$(0.995)(0.990)(0.990) = 0.796$$

The fuel used during phases 1 through 9 is given by Eqn.(2.14) as:

$$W_{F_{used}} = (1 - 0.796)W_{TO} = 0.204 W_{TO}$$

Since the fuel reserves are already accounted for, it is seen that in this case also:

$$W_F = 0.204 W_{TO}$$

Step 4. A tentative value for W_{OE} is found from Eqn.(2.4) as:

$$W_{OE_{tent}} = 130,000 - 0.204 \times 130,000 - 30,750 =$$
$$= 72,730 \text{ lbs}$$

Step 5. The crew weight, $W_{crew} = 1,025$ lbs is

found from the mission specification, Table 2.18.
A tentative value for W_E is found from Eqn.(2.5) as:

$$W_{E_{tent}} = 72,730 - 0.005 \times 130,000 - 1,025 =$$
$$= 71,055 \text{ lbs.}$$

Step 6. The allowable value for W_E is found from

Figure 2.9 (or from Eqn.(2.16) as:

W_E= 70,000 lbs. It is seen that the

difference between W_E and $W_{e_{tent}}$ is

1,055 lbs. This difference is too large.
An iteration is thus needed.

Step 7. Note that the iteration in this example
will have to drive the estimate for W_{TO}

down. It is left to the reader to show,
that a value of W_{TO}= 127,000 lbs does

satisfy the iteration criterion as stated
in Section 2.1, Step 7.

To summarize, the following preliminary numbers
define the airplane with the mission specification of
Table 2.18:

W_{TO}= 127,000 lbs

W_E = 68,450 lbs

W_F = 25,850 lbs

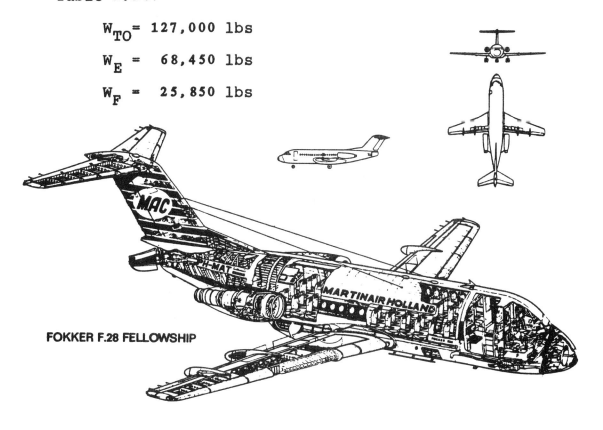

FOKKER F.28 FELLOWSHIP

2.6.3 Example 3: Fighter

Table 2.19 gives an example mission specification for a ground attack fighter airplane. Note that the various mission phases have been numbered. The example follows the step-by-step method outlined in Section 2.1.

Step 1. From Table 2.19, the payload weight, W_{PL}

is: $2,000 + 20 \times 500 = 12,000$ lbs

Step 2. A likely value for W_{TO} is obtained by

examining data for similar airplanes. In Reference 9, the following information is found:

Airplane Type	W_{PL} (lbs)	W_{TO} (lbs)	V_{max} (kts)	Range (nm)
F.R. A10A	15,000	50,000	450	540
Grumman A6	17,000	60,400	689	1,700
Tornado F.Mk2	16,000	58,400	600*	750

* with ext. stores, 1,106 clean!

From these data, an initial guess for W_{TO}

is: $W_{TO_{guess}} = 60,000$ lbs.

Step 3. To determine a value for W_F, the procedure

of Section 2.4 will be followed. Mission phases are defined in Table 2.19.

Phase 1: Engine Start and Warm-up.
Begin weight is W_{TO}. End weight is W_1.

The ratio W_1/W_{TO} is typically 0.990 as

indicated in Table 2.1.

Phase 2: Taxi.
Begin weight is W_1. End weight is W_2.

The ratio W_2/W_1 is typically 0.990 as

indicated by Table 2.1.

Table 2.19 Mission Specification For A Fighter

==

Payload: 20x500 lbs bombs, carried externally and
                    2,000 lbs of ammunition for the GAU-81A
                    multi-barrel cannon. The cannon weight
                    of 4,000 lbs, is part of W_E.

Crew: One pilot (200 lbs).

Range and
Altitude: See mission profile. No reserves.

Cruise Speed: 400 kts at sealevel with external load.
                    450 kts at sealevel, clean.
                    M = 0.80 at 40,000 ft with external load.
                    M = 0.85 at 40,000 ft, clean.
Climb: Direct climb to 40,000 ft. at max. W_{TO}
                    in 8 minutes is desired.
                    Climb rate on one engine, at max. W_{TO}

                    should exceed 500 fpm on a $95°F$ day.

Take-off and
Landing: groundrun of less than 2,400 ft at

                    sealevel and a $95°F$ day.

Powerplants: Two turbofans.

Pressurization: 5,000 ft. cockpit at 50,000 ft.

Certification
Base: Military.

Mission Profile:

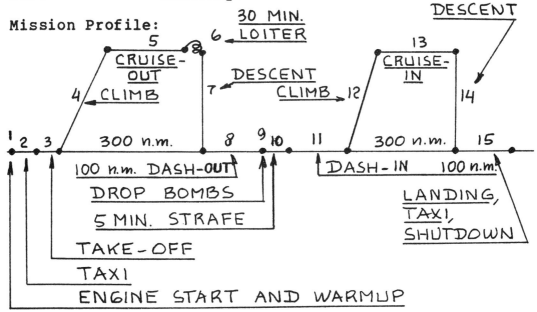

Phase 3. Take-off.
Begin weight is W_2. End weight is W_3.

The ratio W_3/W_2 is typically 0.990 as seen in Table 2.1.

Phase 4. Climb to cruise altitude and accelerate to cruise speed.
Begin weight is W_3. End weight is W_4.

The ratio W_4/W_3 is 0.971 as seen from

Figure 2.2, with V_{cruise}= 459 kts, which

corresponds to M = 0.8 at 40,000 ft.
Range credit needs to be taken, according to the mission profile of Table 2.19. It will be assumed, that the climb is performed at an average speed of 350 kts and with an average climb-rate of 5,000 fpm. To 40,000 ft this takes 8 min. The range covered is (8/60)x350 = 47 nm.

Phase 5. Cruise-out.
Begin weight is W_4. End weight is W_5.

The cruise phase is to be carried out at 40,000 ft and with a speed corresponding to M=0.80 (with ext. load).
This means V_{cruise}=459 kts. Fuel used

during this part of the mission can be estimated from Breguet's range equation:

$$R_{cr}= (V/c_j)_{cr}(L/D)_{cr}\ln(W_4/W_5) \qquad (2.10)$$

The range is 300 - 47 = 253 nm. Because this fighter carries its bomb load externally and because it cruises at a rather high cruise speed, the L/D value during cruise-out is not likely to be very high. A value of 7.0 seems reasonable. For c_j,

Table 2.2 indicates that 0.6 might be an optimistic choice. With these numbers the fuel-fraction for this phase follows from Eqn.(2.10) as: W_5/W_4= 0.954.

Phase 6. Loiter.
Begin weight is W_5. End weight is W_6.

During loiter, the lift-to-drag ratio
will be significantly better than during
high speed cruise-out. A value of 9.0
for $(L/D)_{ltr}$ will be used. For c_j,

Table 2.2 indicates that 0.6 is o.k.
Loiter time is specified at 30 min.
The fuel-fraction for this phase follows
from Breguet's endurance equation:

$$E_{ltr} = (1/c_j)(L/D)_{ltr} \ln(W_5/W_6) \qquad (2.12)$$

This yields: $W_6/W_5 = 0.967$

Phase 7. Descent.
Begin weight is W_6. End weight is W_7.

Table 2.1 suggests that W_7/W_6 is 0.99

No range credit is to be taken, as seen
from the mission profile of Table 2.19.

Phase 8. Dash-out.
Begin weight is W_7. End weight is W_8.

The speed during dash-out is specified as
400 kts in the ext.load configuration.
This means a poor lift-to-drag ratio: a
value of 4.5 will be assumed.
With a range of 100 nm , $c_j = 0.9$ and

L/D = 4.5, the fuel fraction can be found
again with Eqn.(2.10): $W_8/W_7 = 0.951$.

Phase 9. Drop Bombs.
Begin weight is W_8. End weight is W_9.

No fuel penalty is assessed and no range
credit is taken. The ratio $W_9/W_8 = 1.0$.

CAUTION:
The bomb load which is dropped is given
in Table 2.19 as 10,000 lbs.
The total fuel fraction up to this point
in the mission is found as:
$M_{ff_{1-9}} = 0.818$. Therefore, (1 - 0.818) =
0.182 is the fuel used as a fraction of
W_{TO}. The latter was guessed to be:

60,000 lbs. Therefore, just prior to the bomb-drop:
$W = 60,000 \times (1 - 0.182) = 49,080$ lbs.
Immediately after the bomb-drop:
$W = 49,080 - 10,000 = 39,080$ lbs.
Since the next weight ratio is predicated on the weight after bomb-drop, it will be necessary to correct the following fuel-fraction of Phase 10.

Phase 10. Strafe.
Begin weight is W_9. End weight is W_{10}.

Strafing time is defined as 5 min. Assuming that during the strafing phase maximum military thrust is used, c_j is probably high: a value of 0.9 will be assumed. The lift-to-drag ratio will also be poor during this phase. A value of 4.5 will be assumed. Using the loiter equation (2.12), the ratio W_{10}/W_9 can be calculated to be 0.983. This ratio needs to be corrected for the weight change which occurred during bomb-drop. The bomb-drop weight ratio is found as:
$39,080/49,080 = 0.796$.
The corrected ratio W_{10}/W_9 is now found as: $\{1 - (1 - 0.983) \times 0.796\} = 0.986$.

CAUTION:
During the strafing run 2,000 lbs of ammunition is expended. The weight at the end of the strafing run due to fuel consumed is found as:

$39,080 - (1 - 0.983) \times 39,080 = 38,416$ lbs.

After ammo firing this becomes: 36,416 lbs
Again, the following fuel-fraction for Phase 11 will have to be corrected.

Phase 11. Dash-in.
Begin weight is W_{10}. End weight is W_{11}.

During this dash, the fighter is back in a clean configuration. For L/D, a value of 5.5 will be used, while for c_j

0.9 seems reasonable here. The dash-out speed is 450 kts according to the specification in Table 2.19. The range is 100 nm. With Eqn.(2.10) the fuel-fraction is computed as:

$$W_{11}/W_{10} = 0.964.$$

This ratio needs to be corrected again. The weight ratio due to ammo firing is:
36,416/38,416 = 0.948.
The corrected weight ratio, W_{11}/W_{10} is found as:
{1- (1- 0.964)x 0.948} = .966.

Phase 12. Climb to cruise altitude and accelerate to cruise speed.
Begin weight is W_{11}. End weight is W_{12}.

The mission specification in this case calls for a cruise speed of M = 0.85. It will be assumed, that this phase is executed in the same manner as Phase 4. Therefore: $W_{12}/W_{11} = 0.969$ and the

range covered is taken to be 47 nm.

Phase 13. Cruise-in.
Begin weight is W_{12}. End weight is W_{13}.

Cruise-out speed in Table 2.19 is given as M = 0.85 at 40,000 ft or 488 kts
The fighter is now lighter than it was during Phase 5. This makes L/D lower. The fighter is also aerodynamically cleaner, because the external load has been dropped. For L/D a value of 7.5 will be assumed. The range is 253 nm and c_j will be assumed to be 0.6, as for

Phase 5. It is found that:

$$W_{13}/W_{12} = 0.959.$$

Phase 14. Descent.

Begin weight is W_{13}. End weight is W_{14}.

No credit for range is taken. From Table 2.1: $W_{14}/W_{13} = 0.99$.

Phase 15. Landing, Taxi and Shutdown.

Begin weight is W_{14}. End weight is W_{15}.

Table 2.1 suggests: $W_{15}/W_{14} = 0.995$.

The overall mission fuel-fraction follows from Eqn.(2.13) as:

$$M_{ff} = \left\{ \frac{W_{15}W_{14}W_{13}\ldots\ldots W_3 W_2 W_1}{W_{14}W_{13}W_{12}\ldots\ldots W_2 W_1 W_{TO}} \right\} =$$

$$= (0.995)(0.99)(0.959)(0.969)(0.966)(0.986)(1.0) \times$$
$$\times (0.951)(0.99)(0.967)(0.954)(0.971)(0.99)(0.99) \times$$
$$\times (0.99) = 0.713.$$

It must be observed that this value for M_{ff} is already the corrected fuel-fraction.
For mission fuel, W_F it is found that:

$$W_F = (1-0.713) \times 60,000 = 17,220 \text{ lbs.}$$

Step 4. The value for $W_{OE_{tent}}$ follows with the help of Eqn.(2.4) as:

$$W_{OE_{tent}} = 60,000 - 17,220 - 12,000 =$$
$$= 30,780 \text{ lbs.}$$

Step 5. A tentative value for W_E follows with the help of Eqn.(2.5) as:

$$W_{E_{tent}} = 30,780 - 0.005 \times 60,000 - 200 =$$
$$= 30,280.$$

Step 6. The allowable value for W_E is found in Figure 2.11 as: $W_E = 31,000$ lbs.

Step 7. The difference between W_E and $W_{E_{tent}}$ is

seen to be 720 lbs. This difference is too large. An iteration is therefore needed. The reader is asked to show, that after iteration, W_{TO}= 64,500 lbs.

To summarize, the ground attack fighter airplane with the mission specification of Table 2.19 is defined by the following initial weight estimates:

W_{TO}= 64,500 lbs (with external stores)

W_{TO}= 54,500 lbs (without external stores)

W_E = 33,500 lbs

W_F = 18,500 lbs

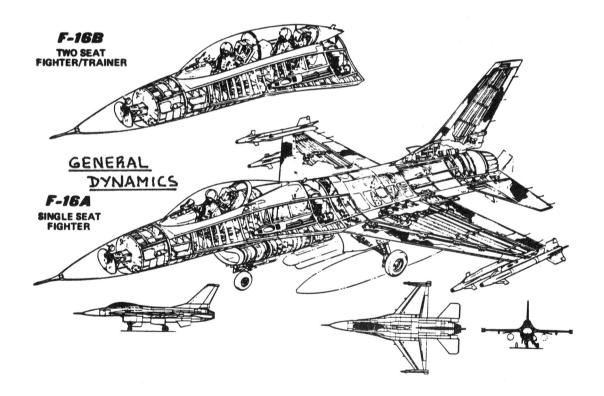

2.7 SENSITIVITY STUDIES AND GROWTH FACTORS

It is evident from the way the results in Section 2.6 were obtained, that their outcome depends on the values selected for the various parameters in the range and endurance equations.

This section will show with some examples, how airplane take-off weight, W_{TO} varies with:

1. Payload, W_{PL}

2. Empty weight, W_E

3. Range, R

4. Endurance, E

5. Lift-to-drag ratio, L/D

6. Specific fuel consumption, c_p or c_j

7. Propeller efficiency, η_p

After preliminary sizing of a new airplane with the methods outlined in Section 2.4, it is mandatory to conduct sensitivity studies on the parameters 1-7 listed before.

The reasons for doing this are:

A. To find out which parameters 'drive' the design
B. To determine which areas of technological change must be pursued, if some new mission capability must be achieved.
C. If parameters 5,6 or 7 were selected optimistically (or pessimistically), the sensitivity studies provide a quick estimate of the impact of such optimism (or pessimism) on the design.

2.7.1 An Analytical Method For Computing Take-off Weight Sensitivities

With the help of Eqns. (2.4) and (2.5), it is possible to write:

$$W_E = W_{TO} - W_F - W_{PL} - W_{tfo} - W_{crew} \qquad (2.17)$$

Equation (2.6) can also be written as:

$$W_F = (1 - M_{ff})W_{TO} + W_{F_{res}} \qquad (2.18)$$

Reserve fuel, $W_{F_{res}}$ can in turn be written as:

$$W_{F_{res}} = M_{res}(1 - M_{ff})W_{TO},\qquad(2.19)$$

where:

M_{res} is the reserve fuel fraction expressed in terms of mission fuel used.

If M_{tfo} is introduced as the trapped fuel and oil fraction expressed in terms of the take-off gross weight, W_{TO}, then it follows that:

$$W_E = W_{TO}\{1 - (1 + M_{res})(1 - M_{ff}) - M_{tfo}\} +$$
$$- (W_{PL} + W_{crew})\qquad(2.20)$$

The latter can in turn be written as:

$$W_E = CW_{TO} - D,\qquad(2.21)$$

where:

$$C = \{1 - (1 + M_{res})(1 - M_{ff}) - M_{tfo}\}\qquad(2.22)$$

and:

$$D = (W_{PL} + W_{crew}) + W_{P_{exp}}\qquad(2.23)$$

The reader is asked to show, that W_E can be eliminated from Eqns.(2.21) and (2.16) to yield:

$$\log_{10}W_{TO} = A + B\log_{10}(CW_{TO} - D)\qquad(2.24)$$

The parameters A and B are the regression line constants of Table 2.15. The parameters C and D are those of Eqns.(2.22) and (2.23).

It is observed, that Eqn.(2.24) also offers the opportunity for a numerical solution to the iteration process discussed in Section 2.4.

If the sensitivity of W_{TO} to some parameter y is desired, it is possible to obtain that sensitivity by partial differentiation of W_{TO} in Eqn.(2.24). This results in:

$$(1/W_{TO})\partial W_{TO}/\partial y =$$

$$B(W_{TO}\partial C/\partial y + C\partial W_{TO}/\partial y - \partial D/\partial y)/(CW_{TO}-D) \qquad (2.25)$$

Since the regression line constants A and B vary only with airplane type, the partial derivatives $\partial A/\partial y$ and $\partial B/\partial y$ are zero.

From Eqn.(2.25) it is possible to solve for $\partial W_{TO}/\partial y$ as:

$$\partial W_{TO}/\partial y =$$

$$\{B(W_{TO})^2\partial C/\partial y - BW_{TO}\partial D/\partial y\}/\{C(1-B)W_{TO}-D\} \qquad (2.26)$$

The parameter y can be any one of those listed as 1-7 at the beginning of this section.

The following sensitivities will now be derived:

2.7.2 Sensitivity of Take-off Weight to Payload Weight

2.7.3 Sensitivity of Take-off Weight to Empty Weight

2.7.4 Sensitivity of Take-off Weight to Range, Endurance, Speed, Specific Fuel Consumption, Propeller Efficiency and Lift-to-Drag Ratio.

2.7.2 Sensitivity of Take-off Weight to Payload Weight

If $y=W_{PL}$, then $\partial D/\partial W_{PL}$ = 1.0 by Eqn.(2.23). Also, $\partial C/\partial W_{PL}$ = 0 by Eqn.(2.22).

Therefore:

$$\partial W_{TO}/\partial W_{PL} = BW_{TO}\{D - C(1-B)W_{TO}\}^{-1} \qquad (2.27)$$

The derivative $\partial W_{TO}/\partial W_{PL}$ is called the airplane growth factor due to payload. Some examples will now be discussed. The examples utilize the airplanes which were discussed in Section 2.6.

2.7.2.1 Example 1: Twin engine propeller driven airplane

For this twin, the following data can be found:

A = 0.0966(Table 2.15)
B = 1.0298(Table 2.15)

C = {1 - 1.25(1 - 0.827) - 0.005} = 0.779
    (See SubSection 2.6.1)
D = 1,250 lbs(Table 2.17)

Note that substitution of A, B, C and D in
Eqn.(2.24) yields:

W_{TO} = 7,935 lbs, which agrees quite well with the

iterative solution found in Par.2.6.1.
    With this value for W_{TO}, it is possible to compute

the sensitivity of W_{TO} to W_{PL} from Eqn.(2.27) as:

$\partial W_{TO} / \partial W_{PL}$ = 5.7.

This means, that for each pound of payload added,
the airplane take-off weight will have to be increased by
5.7 lbs. This assumes, that the mission performance
stays the same. The factor 5.7 is called the growth
factor due to payload for this twin.

2.7.2.2 Example 2: Jet transport

For this jet transport, the following data can be
found:

A = 0.0833(Table 2.15)
B = 1.0383(Table 2.15)
C = {1 - (1 - 0.796) - 0.005} = 0.791
    (See SubSection 2.6.2)
D = 31,775 lbs (Table 2.18)

Note that substitution of A, B, C and D in
Eqn.(2.24) yields:

W_{TO} = 126,100 lbs, which agrees very well with the

iterative solution found in SubSection 2.6.2.
    With this value for W_{TO} it is possible to compute

the sensitivity of W_{TO} to W_{PL} from Eqn.(2.27) as:

$\partial W_{TO} / \partial W_{PL}$ = 3.7

This means that for each pound of payload added, the
airplane take-off gross weight will have to be increased
by 3.7 lbs. This assumes, that the mission performance
stays the same. In this case the factor 3.7 is called
the growth factor due to payload for this jet transport.

2.7.2.3 Example 3: Fighter

For this fighter, the following data can be found:

A = 0.5091(Table 2.15)
B = 0.9505(Table 2.15)
C = {1 - (1 - 0.713) - 0.005} = 0.708
    (See SubSection 2.6.3)
D = 12,200 lbs(Table 2.18)

Note, that substitution of A, B, C and D into Eqn.(2.24) yields:

W_{TO}= 64,000 lbs, which agrees quite well with the

iterative solution found in SubSection 2.6.3.

With this value of W_{TO} it is possible to compute

the sensitivity of W_{TO} to W_{PL} from Eqn.(2.27) as:

$$\partial W_{TO}/\partial W_{PL}= 6.1$$

This means that for each pound of payload added, the airplane take-off gross weight will have to be increased by 6.1 lbs. This assumes, that mission performance is kept the same. The factor 6.1 is called the growth factor due to payload for this fighter.

2.7.3 Sensitivity of Take-off Weight to Empty Weight

From Eqn.(2.16) it follows that:

$$\log_{10}W_{TO} = A + B\log_{10}W_E \qquad (2.28)$$

By partial differentiation of W_{TO} with respect to

W_E the take-off weight to empty weight sensitivity is

expressed as:

$$\partial W_{TO}/\partial W_E= BW_{TO}[invlog_{10}\{(\log_{10}W_{TO} - A)/B\}]^{-1} \qquad (2.29)$$

To illustrate the meaning of Eqn.(2.29), three examples will be discussed. The airplanes used are those of Section 2.6.

2.7.3.1 Example 1: Twin engine propeller driven airplane

For this airplane, the following values were previously found:

A = 0.0966(Table 2.15)
B = 1.0298(Table 2.15)
W_{TO}= 7,935 lbs(See 2.7.2.1)

Eqn.(2.29) yields with these data:

$\partial W_{TO}/\partial W_E$= 1.66

For each lbs of increase in empty weight, the take-off weight must be increased by 1.66 lbs, to keep the mission performance the same. The factor 1.66 is the growth factor due to empty weight for this twin.

2.7.3.2 Example 2: Jet transport

For the jet tranport, the following data were previously found:

A = 0.0833(Table 2.15)
B = 1.0383(Table 2.15)
W_{TO}= 126,100 lbs(See 2.7.2.2)

Eqn.(2.29) produces with these data:

$\partial W_{TO}/\partial W_E$= 1.93

For each pound of increase in empty weight, the take-off weight must be increased by 1.93 lbs, to keep the mission performance the same. The factor 1.93 is the growth factor due to empty weight for this jet transport.

2.7.3.3 Example 3: Fighter

For this fighter airplane, the following data were previously determined:

A = 0.5091(Table 2.15)
B = 0.9505(Table 2.15)
W_{TO}= 64,000 lbs(See 2.7.2.3)

It is found with Eqn.(2.29) and these data that:

$\partial W_{TO}/\partial W_E$= 1.83

For each pound of increase in empty weight, the take-off weight must be increased by 1.83 lbs, to keep the mission performance the same. The factor 1.83 is the growth factor due to empty weight for this fighter.

2.7.4 Sensitivity of Take-off Weight to Range, Endurance, Speed, Specific Fuel Consumption, Propeller Efficiency and Lift-to-Drag Ratio

In this sub-section the parameters Range, R, Endurance, E, Speed, V, Specific Fuel Consumption, c_p and c_j, Propeller Efficiency, η_p and Lift-to-Drag Ratio, L/D are represented by the symbol y.

The sensitivity of W_{TO} to any parameter y, <u>which is not payload</u>, W_{PL} is found from Eqn.(2.26) as:

$$\partial W_{TO}/\partial y = \{CW_{TO}(1 - B) - D\}^{-1} BW_{TO}{}^2 \partial C/\partial y \qquad (2.30)$$

where C is defined by Eqn.(2.22) which can also be written as:

$$C = \{M_{ff}(1 + M_{res}) - M_{tfo} - M_{res}\} \qquad (2.31)$$

Partial differentiation with respect to y gives:

$$\partial C/\partial y = (1 + M_{res})\partial M_{ff}/\partial y \qquad (2.32)$$

As was seen in the examples of the fighter and the jet transport, the reserve fraction M_{res} is often zero, because the reserves were included in the mission profile.

For the twin propeller, this was not the case and the value for M_{res} was 0.25. The reader should carefully inspect the mission specification, before assigning a value to M_{res}.

The differential $\partial M_{ff}/\partial y$ can be found from Eqn.(2.13) as:

$$\partial M_{ff}/\partial y = M_{ff}(W_i/W_{i+1})\partial(W_{i+1}/W_i)/\partial y \qquad (2.33)$$

At this point, it is recalled that the ratio W_i/W_{i+1} can be determined from Breguet's equations. These Breguet equations take on two different forms, depending on whether range or endurance is sought. Breguet's equations can be generalized as:

$$\bar{R} = \ln(W_i/W_{i+1}) \qquad (2.34)$$

or as:

$$\bar{E} = \ln(W_i/W_{i+1}) \tag{2.35}$$

The quantities $\bar{R}$ and $\bar{E}$ in turn are found as follows:

For propeller driven airplanes:

$$\bar{R} = Rc_p(375\eta_p L/D)^{-1} \tag{2.36}$$

$$\bar{E} = EVc_p(375\eta_p L/D)^{-1} \tag{2.37}$$

For jet airplanes:

$$\bar{R} = Rc_j(VL/D)^{-1} \tag{2.38}$$

$$\bar{E} = Ec_j(L/D)^{-1} \tag{2.39}$$

The reader is asked to show that equations (2.34) and (2.35) can be differentiated to yield:

$$\partial(W_{i+1}/W_i)/\partial y = -(W_{i+1}/W_i)\partial\bar{R}/\partial y \tag{2.40}$$

and:

$$\partial(W_{i+1}/W_i)/\partial y = -(W_{i+1}/W_i)\partial\bar{E}/\partial y \tag{2.41}$$

respectively.

By combining Eqns.(2.30), (2.32), and (2.33) with (2.40) or (2.41), the sensitivity of W_{TO} with respect to y can be written as:

$$\partial W_{TO}/\partial y = F\partial\bar{R}/\partial y \tag{2.42}$$

for the case involving a ratio (W_{i+1}/W_i) dependent on range, and:

$$\partial W_{TO}/\partial y = F\partial\bar{E}/\partial y \tag{2.43}$$

for the case involving a ratio (W_{i+1}/W_i) dependent on endurance.

The factor F in these equations is defined as:

$$F = - BW_{TO}^2\{CW_{TO}(1 - B) - D\}^{-1}(1 + M_{res})M_{ff} \tag{2.44}$$

The form taken by the so-called Breguet partials

$\partial \overline{R} / \partial y$ and $\partial \overline{E} / \partial y$ depends on whether the particular weight ratio being differentiated is defined by Eqn.(2.34) or by Eqn.(2.35). Table 2.20 gives the forms for the Breguet partials. These partials are derived by partially differentiating Eqns. (2.36) through (2.39) with respect to R, E, V, c_p, c_j, η_p or L/D.

2.7.5 Examples of Sensitivities to Range, Endurance and Speed

Range, R, endurance, E and speed, V are all items which are normally specified in the mission specification. Since mission specifications are often open to negotiation, it is of great interest to be able to determine how these items affect the design gross weight, W_{TO} of an airplane.

This sub-section will show with examples, how the sensitivity of W_{TO} to changes in R, E and V can be found.

Implications for the design of the airplane will be indicated.

By setting R, E and V sequentially equal to y it is possible to calculate the sensitivity of W_{TO} to these parameters from Eqns.(2.42) and (2.43). The corresponding Breguet Partials $\partial \overline{R} / \partial y$ and $\partial \overline{E} / \partial y$ can be found from Table 2.20.

2.7.5.1 Example 1: Twin engine propeller driven airplane

First it is noted from the mission specification of Table 2.17 that no value for E was specified. Also, it is observed, that R, for a propeller driven airplane does not depend on V. Therefore, the only sensitivity to be computed here is $\partial W_{TO} / \partial R$.

The reader is asked to show, that the take-off weight to range sensitivity in this case can be found from:

$$\partial W_{TO} / \partial R = F c_p (375 \eta_p L/D)^{-1}, \tag{2.45}$$

where F is defined by Eqn.(2.44).
For this twin, the following data are found:

B = 1.0298 (Table 2.15) M_{res} = 0.25 (incl. in M_{ff})
C = 0.779   (2.7.2.1)

Table 2.20 Breguet Partials for Propeller Driven and for Jet Airplanes

		Propeller Driven	Jet
Range Case	$y = R$	$\partial\bar{R}/\partial y = c_p(375\eta_p L/D)^{-1}$	$\partial\bar{R}/\partial y = c_j(VL/D)^{-1}$
Endurance Case	$y = E$	$\partial\bar{E}/\partial y = Vc_p(375\eta_p L/D)^{-1}$	$\partial\bar{E}/\partial y = c_j(L/D)^{-1}$
Range Case	$y = c_p$ ($y = c_j$)	$\partial\bar{R}/\partial y = R(375\eta_p L/D)^{-1}$	$\partial\bar{R}/\partial y = R(VL/D)^{-1}$
Endurance Case	$y = c_p$ ($y = c_j$)	$\partial\bar{E}/\partial y = EV(375\eta_p L/D)^{-1}$	$\partial\bar{E}/\partial y = E(L/D)^{-1}$
Range Case	$y = \eta_p$	$\partial\bar{R}/\partial y = -Rc_p(375\eta_p^2 L/D)^{-1}$	Not Applicable
Endurance Case	$y = \eta_p$	$\partial\bar{E}/\partial y = -EVc_p(375\eta_p^2 L/D)^{-1}$	Not Applicable
Range Case	$y = V$	Not Applicable	$\partial\bar{R}/\partial y = -Rc_j(V^2 L/D)^{-1}$
Endurance Case	$y = V$	$\partial\bar{E}/\partial y = Ec_p(375\eta_p L/D)^{-1}$	Not Applicable
Range Case	$y = L/D$	$\partial\bar{R}/\partial y = -Rc_p(375\eta_p(L/D)^2)^{-1}$	$\partial\bar{R}/\partial y = -Rc_j(V(L/D)^2)^{-1}$
Endurance Case	$y = L/D$	$\partial\bar{E}/\partial y = -EVc_p(375\eta_p(L/D)^2)^{-1}$	$\partial\bar{E}/\partial y = -Ec_j(L/D)^{-2}$

Note: R in sm
V in mph

Note: R in nm or sm
V in kts or mph

D = 1,250 lbs (Table 2.17) M_{ff}= 0.827 (2.6.1)
W_{TO}= 7,935 lbs (2.7.2.1)

c_p= 0.5, η_p= 0.82, L/D = 11 as given in 2.7.2.1.

With these data substituted into Eqn.(2.44) it is found that:

F = 46,736 lbs.

From Eqn.(2.45) it now follows that:

$\partial W_{TO}/\partial R$ = 6.9 lbs/sm.

The significance of this partial is as follows. Suppose that the range in the mission specification of Table 2.17 is changed from 1,000 nm to 1,100 nm. The result just found indicates that this would require an increase in gross weight at take-off of 100x6.9 = 690 lbs.

2.7.5.2 Example 2: Jet transport

The mission specification for the jet transport is given in Table 2.18. It is seen that both range and endurance are specified. Therefore the sensitivities of W_{TO} to both R and to E need to be calculated.

For the jet transport, the following data are found:

B = 1.0383 (Table 2.15) M_{res}= 0 (incl in M_{ff})
C = 0.791 (2.7.2.2)
D = 31,775 lbs (Table 2.18) M_{ff}= 0.796 (2.6.2)

W_{TO}= 126,100 lbs (2.7.2.2) F = 369,211 lbs
(Eqn.(2.44))
for cruise:
c_j= 0.5, L/D = 16 and V = 473 kts as given in

Sub-section 2.6.2.

for endurance:
c_j= 0.6, L/D = 18 as given in Sub-section 2.6.2.

The reader is asked to verify, that the sensitivities of take-off gross weight to range and to endurance can be written as:

$$\partial W_{TO}/\partial R = Fc_j(VL/D)^{-1} \qquad (2.46)$$

and:

$$\partial W_{TO} / \partial E = Fc_j (L/D)^{-1}, \qquad\qquad (2.47)$$

where F is again given by Eqn.(2.44).

When the jet transport data are substituted into Eqns. (2.46) and (2.47), the following sensitivities are found:

$$\partial W_{TO} / \partial R = 24.4 \text{ lbs/nm, and:}$$

$$\partial W_{TO} / \partial E = 12,307 \text{ lbs/hr.}$$

The significance of these sensitivities is as follows. If the range in the mission specification of Table 2.18 is decreased from 1,500 nm to 1,400 nm, the take-off gross weight can be decreased by 100x24.4 = 2,440 lbs. Similarly, if the loiter requirement of Table 2.18 is increased from 1 hour to 1.5 hours, the take-off gross weight will be increased by 1/2x12,307 = 6,154 lbs.

The transport is also sensitive to the specification of cruise speed. Since cruise speed has a major impact on block-speed, it will be necessary to compute the sensitivity of take-off gross weight to cruise speed. The reader is asked to verify that:

$$\partial W_{TO} / \partial V = -FRc_j (V^2 L/D)^{-1}, \qquad\qquad (2.48)$$

where F is defined in Eqn.(2.44).

With the data at the beginning of this example substituted into Eqn.(2.48) it is found that:

$$\partial W_{TO} / \partial V = -74.1 \text{ lbs/kt.}$$

What this means, is that if the cruise speed could be increased without changing any of the other parameters, the gross weight would actually come down. From a mathematical viewpoint, this result is correct. From a practical viewpoint _it is not._ There are several reasons for this. When the cruise speed is increased, the cruise lift coefficient is decreased. This usually means a decrease in L/D. It also usually means a change in c_j. Finally, there is the effect of increased Mach

number on L/D. This also tends to decrease L/D.

2.7.5.3 Example 3: Fighter

From the mission specification of Table 2.19 it is seen, that the fighter has range, endurance and speed sensitivity. Because the mission profile consists of several range phases and an endurance phase, it will be necessary to calculate the sensitivities with respect to these phases separately.

The reader is asked to verify, that the sensitivities of fighter take-off gross weight to changes in range and endurance can be computed also from Eqns. (2.46) and (2.47). For the fighter, the following data can be found:

B = 0.9505 (Table 2.15) M_{res}= 0 (mission spec.
C = 0.708 (2.7.2.3)   shows no reserves)
D = 12,200 lbs (Table 2.19) M_{ff}= 0.713 (2.7.2.3)

W_{TO}= 64,000 (2.7.2.3)   F = 278,786 lbs
                                              (Eqn.(2.44))

Values for c_j, V and L/D vary with each mission phase. The following tabulation shows these numbers as found in (2.7.2.3) and also shows the corresponding sensitivities.

	Cruise-out	Dash-out	Dash-in	Cruise-in	Loiter
c_j	0.6	0.9	0.9	0.6	0.6
V	459	400	450	488	N.A.
L/D	7.0	4.5	5.5	7.5	9.0
$\partial W_{TO}/\partial R$	52.1	139	101	45.7	N.A.
$\partial W_{TO}/\partial E$	N.A.	N.A.	N.A.	N.A.	18,586

It is clear from these data, that the dash-out part of the mission has the greatest sensitivity of W_{TO} to range. If there is a military need to increase the dash-out range from 100 nm to 200 nm, the consequence is an increase of take-off gross weight of 100x139 = 13,900 lbs. At the current fighter cost of 500 dollars/lbs, that would increase the unit cost of the fighter by 7.0 million dollars! It will be clear to the reader, that military need and affordability must be traded against each other in the final definition of the mission specification.

It is also clear from the data, that if the loiter time of 30 min could be cut to 15 min. (such as by improved C^3I), the take-off gross weight would decrease by 0.25x18,586 = 4,645 lbs. This would result in a decrease in unit cost of 2.3 million dollars!

2.7.6 Examples of Sensitivities to Specific Fuel Consumption, Propeller Efficiency and Lift-to-Drag Ratio

Specific fuel consumption, c_p or c_j, propeller efficiency, η_p and lift-to-drag ratio, L/D are all items which the designer has under his control to the extent of the existing state of technology. The fuel consumption is dependent on the state of engine technology. Propeller efficiency depends on the state of propeller technology. Airplane lift-to-drag ratio depends on the aerodynamic configuration, the method used to integrate the propulsion system into the configuration and on the state of aerodynamic technology (for example laminar versus turbulent boundary layers).

Sensitivities of gross weight at take-off to these factors must be evaluated for the following reasons:

1. A large sensitivity may force a different configuration design approach. Higher wing loading, different schemes of propulsion system integration or different engine choices may result.

2. It is quite possible that the sensitivity results lead to the establishment of improvement targets in these factors. Sometimes such improvements can be brought about by a directed research and development program.

The purpose of this sub-section is to illustrate, with examples, how the sensitivity of W_{TO} to these factors can be computed.

2.7.6.1 Example 1: Twin engine propeller driven airplane

For this airplane, the sensitivity of W_{TO} to the parameters c_p, η_p and L/D needs to be determined.

Because the mission specification for this twin (Table 2.17) does not specify a requirement for endurance, only the range dependent Breguet Partials in Table 2.20 are needed.

The reader is asked to show that the sensitivity of take-off gross weight to specific fuel consumption can be obtained from:

$$\partial W_{TO}/\partial c_p = FR(375\eta_p L/D)^{-1}, \qquad (2.49)$$

where F is defined by Eqn.(2.44).

The required data for the twin were already given in (2.7.5.1). The value for range, R is 1000 nm, according to Table 2.18.

Eqn. (2.49) yields in this case:

$$\partial W_{TO}/\partial c_p = 13,817 \text{ lbs/lbs/hp/hr.}$$

The significance of this finding is as follows. Suppose an engine could be found with a c_p of 0.45 instead of 0.50. The take-off gross weight of this twin could then be decreased by 0.05x13,817 = 691 lbs.

The sensitivity of take-off gross weight to propeller efficiency can be calculated from:

$$\partial W_{TO}/\partial \eta_p = -FRc_p(375\eta_p^2 L/D)^{-1}, \qquad (2.50)$$

where F is given by Eqn.(2.44)

Using the previous data in Eqn.(2.50) yields:

$$\partial W_{TO}/\partial \eta_p = -8,425 \text{ lbs.}$$

The meaning of this finding is as follows. If the propeller efficiency could be increased from 0.82 to 0.84, the take-off gross weight would decrease by 0.02x8,425 = 168 lbs.

The sensitivity of take-off gross weight to lift-to-drag ratio can be computed from:

$$\partial W_{TO}/\partial (L/D) = -FRc_p\{375\eta_p (L/D)^2\}^{-1}, \qquad (2.51)$$

where F is again given by Eqn.(2.44).

Substituting the previous data into Eqn.(2.51) results in:

$$\partial W_{TO}/\partial (L/D) = -628 \text{ lbs.}$$

This result means, that if L/D could be increased from 11 to 12, the take-off gross weight would come down by 628 lbs. It comes as no surprise, that L/D in a range dominated airplane has a powerful effect on gross weight.

2.7.6.2 Example 2: Jet transport

In the case of the jet transport, the sensitivities of take-off gross weight to specific fuel consumption and to L/D need to be determined. Since the mission specification calls for both range and loiter, two sensitivities need to be looked at for each parameter.

The reader is asked to verify that:

With respect to the range requirement:

$$\partial W_{TO}/\partial c_j = FR(VL/D)^{-1} \qquad (2.52)$$

$$\partial W_{TO}/\partial(L/D) = - FRc_j(V(L/D)^2)^{-1} \qquad (2.53)$$

With respect to the loiter requirement:

$$\partial W_{TO}/\partial c_j = FE(L/D)^{-1} \qquad (2.54)$$

$$\partial W_{TO}/\partial(L/D) = - FEc_j(L/D)^{-2} \qquad (2.55)$$

From previous data in (2.7.5.2) it is found that F = 369,211 lbs in this instance.

<u>For the range case</u>, this yields the following sensitivities:

$$\partial W_{TO}/\partial c_j =$$

369,211x0.190 = 70,056 lbs/lbs/lbs/hr.

and:

$$\partial W_{TO}/\partial(L/D) = 369,211x(- 0.00593) = - 2,189 \text{ lbs.}$$

These numbers have the following implications:

1. If specific fuel consumption was incorrectly assumed to be 0.5 and in reality turns out to be 0.8, the design take-off gross weight will increase by 0.3x70,056 = 21,017 lbs.

2. If the lift-to-drag ratio of the airplane were 17 instead of the assumed 16, the design take-off gross weight would decrease by 2,189 lbs.

<u>For the loiter case</u>, the following sensitivities are found:

$$\partial W_{TO}/\partial c_j =$$

369,211x0.0556 = 20,512 lbs/lbs/lbs/hr.

and:

$$\partial W_{TO}/\partial(L/D) = 369,211x(- 0.001852) = - 684 \text{ lbs.}$$

These numbers have the following significance:

1. If the specific fuel consumption during loiter could be improved from the assumed value of 0.6 to 0.5, the take-off gross weight would decrease by 0.1x20,512 = 2,051 lbs.

2. If the lift-to-drag ratio during loiter could be improved from the assumed value of 18 to 19, the take-off gross weight would be reduced by 684 lbs.

These sensitivity data show again how sensitive the take-off gross weight of a range-dominated airplane is to L/D and to specific fuel consumption.

2.7.6.3 Example 3: Fighter

For the fighter, with four range type mission phases and one endurance type mission phase, a range of sensitivities need to be computed. Equations (2.52), (2.53), (2.54) and (2.55) also apply to this fighter.

The value of F in these equations was previously determined to be 278,786 lbs. The following tabulation shows the sensitivities for the five important mission phases.

	Cruise-out	Dash-out	Dash-in	Cruise-in	Loiter
c_j	0.6	0.9	0.9	0.6	0.6
V(kts)	459	400	450	488	N.A.
L/D	7.0	4.5	5.5	7.5	9.0
R(nm)	253	100	100	253	N.A.
E(hr)	N.A.	N.A.	N.A.	N.A.	0.5
$\partial W_{TO}/\partial c_j$	21,952	15,488	11,264	19,271	15,488
	<	Eqn.(2.52)		><Eqn.(2.54)>	
$\partial W_{TO}/\partial (L/D)$	-1,882	-3,098	-1,843	-1,542	-1,033
	<	Eqn.(2.53)		><Eqn.(2.55)>	

Implications of these results will now be discussed. An improvement in sfc by 0.1 in the dash-out part of the mission would save 0.1x15,488 = 1,549 lbs in take-off gross weight. An increase in L/D by 0.5 in the cruise-out part of the mission would result in a decrease in take-off gross weight of 0.5x1,882 = 941 lbs.

2.8 PROBLEMS

1.) For the jet transport example of 2.6.2 redo the mission fuel-fraction analysis by splitting the cruise phase (Phase 5) into five equal distances. Account for the estimated weight changes due to fuel consumption by adjusting the L/D to the average weight which prevails during each sub-phase. Keep the cruise Mach number and the cruise altitude as in Table 2.18. Assume that the drag polar of the airplane is:

$$C_D = 0.0200 + 0.0333C_L^2 .$$

Compute the sensitivities of W_{TO} to C_{D_0}.

2.) A regional transport has the following mission specification:

Payload:	34 passengers at 175 lbs each and 30 lbs of baggage each.
Crew:	two pilots and one cabin attendant.
Range:	four consecutive trips of 250 nm: R_1 through R_4, with max. payload.
	Reserves for flight to an alternate airport, 100 nm. away, followed by 45 min. loiter.
Altitude:	25,000 ft for design mission.
Cruise speed:	250 kts.
Climb:	Climb to 25,000 ft in 10 min.
Take-off and landing:	FAR 25 fieldlength, 5,000 ft at an altitude of 5,000 ft and a 95°F day. Assume that $W_L = 0.9W_{TO}$.
Powerplants:	Two turboprops or propfans.
Pressurization:	5,000 ft cabin at 35,000 ft.
Certification Base:	FAR 25.

Determine W_{TO}, W_E and W_F for this airplane.

Compute the sensitivities of W_{TO} to c_p, η_p,

and to L/D. Find how W_{TO} varies if the range segment

is changed from 250 nm to 200 nm and to 300 nm.

3.) A high altitude loiter and reconnaissance airplane has the following mission specification:

Payload: 3,000 lbs of avionics equipment and a
                        rotating external antenna (equivalent
                        to that on the Grumman E2C) with
                        a weight of 3,500 lbs.
Crew: Two pilots, one avionics systems opera-
                        tor plus a relief crew of three. Use
                        200 lbs per crewmember.
Range: 1500 nm from a coastal base, followed by
                        48 hours of loiter on station, followed
                        by return to base. No reserves.

Altitude: Loiter altitude: 45,000 ft. Must be
                        able to maintain station with 120 kts
                        wind.
Cruise speed: Larger than 250 kts desired.
Climb: Must be able to climb to 45,000 ft at
                        arrival on loiter station.
Take-off and
Landing: 5,000 ft groundrun, standard day, sea-
                        level at maximum take-off weight and at
                        maximum landing weight respectively.
                        Assume that $W_L = 0.75W_{TO}$.

Powerplants: Propfans. At least two engines.
Pressurization: 5,000 ft cabin at 45,000 ft.
Certification
Base: Military.
Note: To save weight, it is acceptable to
                        set the limit loadfactor at 2.0 instead
                        of the usual 2.5, for the outgoing leg
                        of the mission. Upon arrival at the
                        loiter station, limit loadfactor should
                        be the standard 2.5.

Determine W_{TO}, W_E and W_F for this airplane.

Calculate the sensitivities of W_{TO} to R, E, L/D and

to c_p and η_p.

Determine how W_{TO} changes, if the loiter station is

2000 nm and 1000 nm from base. Also find W_{TO} for loiter

times of 24, 36 and 50 hours. How would W_{TO} change, if
L/D could be improved by 30 percent?

4.) A homebuilt composite airplane has the following mission specification:

Payload: Two pilots at 175 lbs each and 30 lbs of baggage each.
Range: 800 nm, reserves for 200 nm flight to alternate airport.
Altitude: 10,000 ft for the design range.
Cruise Speed: 250 kts at 10,000 ft.
Climb: 10 min. to 10,000 ft.
Take-off and
Landing: 2,500 ft fieldlength.
Powerplant: Piston-propeller, single engine.
Pressurization: None.
Certification
Base: Experimental. Use FAR 23 for Take-off and landing.

Determine W_{TO}, W_E and W_F for this airplane.

Calculate the sensitivity of W_{TO} to R, c_p and η_p.

5.) A supersonic cruise airplane has the following mission specification:

Payload: 300 passengers at 175 lbs each and 30 lbs of baggage each.
Crew: Two pilots and ten cabin attendants at 175 lbs each and 30 lbs baggage each.
Range: 3,500 nm, followed by 1 hour loiter, followed by a 100 nm flight to an alternate airport.
Altitude: 75,000 ft (for the design range).
Cruise Speed: Mach 2.7.
Climb: Direct to 75,000 ft at W_{TO}.
Take-off and
Landing: 10,000 ft FAR fieldlength, 95° day, at sealevel.
                   Assume that $W_L = 0.8W_{TO}$.

Powerplants: At least three turbofans. These could be fitted for afterburning, if needed.
Pressurization: 7,500 ft cabin at 75,000 ft.
                   Certification
Base: FAR 25.

Determine W_{TO}, W_E and W_F for this airplane.

Find the sensitivities of W_{TO} to cruise range and to specific fuel consumption.

6.) A high altitude, unmanned communications airplane has the following mission specification:

Payload:	2,000 lbs.
Crew:	Not applicable.
Range:	1,000 nm out and 1,000 nm in.
	No reserves.
Endurance:	168 hours (= 7 days) on station.
Cruise Speed:	250 kts is desired.
Loiter Altitude:	85,000 ft.
Loiter Speed:	At least 35 kts, to cope with
	prevailing winds.
Take-off and	
Landing:	8,000 ft groundrun is acceptable.
	Assume that $W_L = 0.65 W_{TO}$.
Powerplants:	Up to designer. Fuel must be JP4 or 5.

Determine W_{TO}, W_E and W_F for this vehicle.

Show how sensitive the vehicle is to changes in L/D, E and c_j or to c_p and η_p.

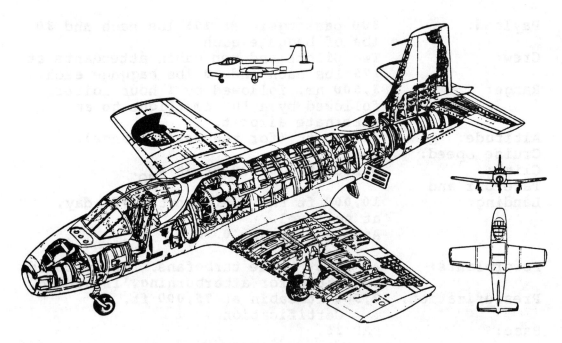

FOKKER S.14 'MACH TRAINER'

3. ESTIMATING WING AREA, S, TAKE-OFF THRUST, T_{TO} (OR TAKE-OFF POWER, P_{TO}) AND MAXIMUM LIFT COEFFICIENT, $C_{L_{max}}$: CLEAN, TAKE-OFF AND LANDING

In addition to meeting range, endurance and cruise speed objectives, airplanes are usually designed to meet performance objectives in the following categories:

a. Stall speed
b. Take-off field length
c. Landing field length
d. Cruise speed (sometimes maximum speed)
e. Climb rate (all engines operating, AEO and one engine inoperative, OEI)
f. Time to climb to some altitude
g. Maneuvering

In this chapter, methods will be presented which allow the rapid estimation of those airplane design parameters which have a major impact on the performance categories a) through g). The airplane design parameters are:

1. Wing Area, S

2. Take-off Thrust, T_{TO} or Take-off Power, P_{TO}

3. Maximum Required Take-off Lift Coefficient with flaps up: $C_{L_{max}}$ (clean)

4. Maximum Required Lift Coefficient for Take-off, $C_{L_{max_{TO}}}$

5. Maximum Required Lift Coefficient for Landing, $C_{L_{max_L}}$, or $C_{L_{max_{PA}}}$

The methods will result in the determination of a range of values of wing loading, W/S, thrust loading, T/W (or power loading, W/P) and maximum lift coefficient, $C_{L_{max}}$, within which certain performance requirements are met. From these data it usually follows that the combination of the highest possible wing loading and the lowest possible thrust loading (or power loading) which still meets all performance requirements results in an airplane with the lowest weight and the lowest cost.

Since W_{TO} was already determined with the methods of Chapter 2, it is clear that now S and T_{TO} can also be determined.

3.1 SIZING TO STALL SPEED REQUIREMENTS

For some airplanes the mission task demands a stall speed not higher than some minimum value. In such a case, the mission specification will include a requirement for a minimum stall speed.

FAR 23 certified single engine airplanes may not have a stall speed greater than 61 kts at W_{TO}.

In addition, FAR 23 certified multiengine airplanes with $W_{TO} < 6,000$ lbs must also have a stall speed of no more than 61 kts, unless they meet certain climb gradient criteria (Ref.8, Par.23.49).

These stall speed requirements can be met flaps-up or flaps-down at the option of the designer.

There are no requirements for minimum stall speed in the case of FAR 25 certified airplanes.

The power-off stall speed of an airplane may be determined from:

$$V_S = \{2(W/S)/\rho C_{L_{max}}\}^{1/2} \tag{3.1}$$

By specifying a maximum allowable stall speed at some altitude, Eqn.(3.1) defines a maximum allowable wing loading W/S for a given value of $C_{L_{max}}$.

Table 3.1 presents typical values of $C_{L_{max}}$ for different types of airplanes with associated flap settings.

The reader should recognize the fact that $C_{L_{max}}$ is strongly influenced by such factors as:

1. Wing and airfoil design
2. Flap type and flap size
3. Center of gravity location

Table 3.1 Typical Values For Maximum Lift Coefficient

===

Airplane Type	$C_{L_{max}}$	$C_{L_{max_{TO}}}$	$C_{L_{max_{L}}}$
1. Homebuilts	1.2 - 1.8	1.2 - 1.8	1.2 - 2.0*
2. Single Engine Propeller Driven	1.3 - 1.9	1.3 - 1.9	1.6 - 2.3
3. Twin Engine Propeller Driven	1.2 - 1.8	1.4 - 2.0	1.6 - 2.5
4. Agricultural	1.3 - 1.9	1.3 - 1.9	1.3 - 1.9
5. Business Jets	1.4 - 1.8	1.6 - 2.2	1.6 - 2.6
6. Regional TBP	1.5 - 1.9	1.7 - 2.1	1.9 - 3.3
7. Transport Jets	1.2 - 1.8	1.6 - 2.2	1.8 - 2.8
8. Military Trainers	1.2 - 1.8	1.4 - 2.0	1.6 - 2.2
9. Fighters	1.2 - 1.8	1.4 - 2.0	1.6 - 2.6
10. Mil. Patrol, Bomb and Transports	1.2 - 1.8	1.6 - 2.2	1.8 - 3.0
11. Flying Boats, Amphibious and Float Airplanes	1.2 - 1.8	1.6 - 2.2	1.8 - 3.4
12. Supersonic Cruise Airplanes	1.2 - 1.8	1.6 - 2.0	1.8 - 2.2

* The Rutan Varieze reaches 2.5, based on stall speed data from Ref.9.

Notes: 1. The data in this table reflect existing (1984) flap design practice.
   2. Considerably higher values for maximum lift coefficient are possible with more sophisticated flap designs and/or with some form of circulation control.
   3. Methods for computing $C_{L_{max}}$ values are contained in Ref.6.

Reference 5 presents methods for computing $C_{L_{max}}$ while accounting for these three factors.

During the preliminary sizing process it suffices to 'select' a value for $C_{L_{max}}$ consistent with the mission requirements and consistent with the type of flaps to be employed.

An example of stall speed sizing will now be discussed.

3.1.1 Example of Stall Speed Sizing

Assume that the following marketing requirement must be met:

A propeller driven airplane must have a power-off stall speed of no more than 50 kts at sealevel with flaps full down (i.e. landing flaps). With flaps up the stall speed is to be less than 60 kts. Both requirements are to be met at take-off gross weight, W_{TO}.

From Table 3.1 it is seen that the following maximum lift coefficient values are within the 'state-of-the-art':

$$C_{L_{max}} = 1.60 \text{ and } C_{L_{max_L}} = 2.00$$

With the help of Eqn.(3.1) it now follows that:

To meet the flaps down requirement:
$(W/S)_{TO} < 17.0$ psf.

To meet the flaps up requirement:
$(W/S)_{TO} < 19.5$ psf.

Therefore, to meet both requirements, the take-off wing loading, $(W/S)_{TO}$ must be less than 17.0 psf.

Figure 3.1 illustrates this. Because the stall speed requirement was formulated as a power-off requirement, neither power loading nor thrust loading are important in this case.

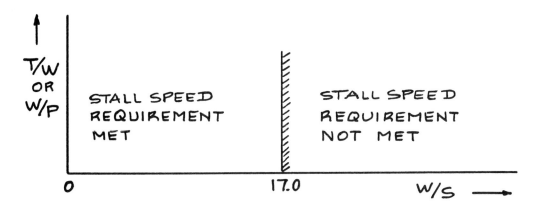

Figure 3.1 Example of Stall Speed Sizing

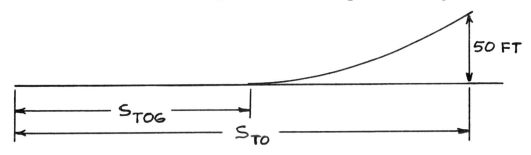

Figure 3.2 Definition of FAR 23 Take-off Distances

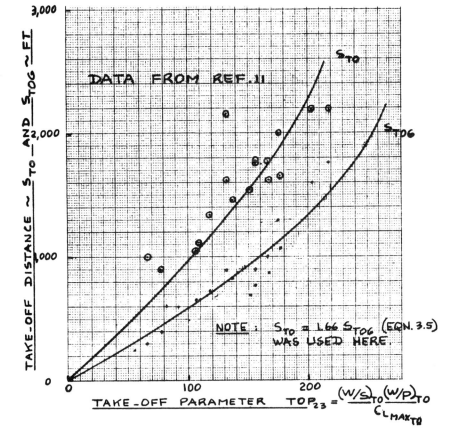

NOTE: $S_{TO} = 1.66\, S_{TOG}$ (EQN. 3.5) WAS USED HERE.

TAKE-OFF PARAMETER $TOP_{23} = \dfrac{(W/S)_{TO}(W/P)_{TO}}{C_{L_{MAX_{TO}}}}$

Figure 3.3 Effect of Take-off Parameter, TOP_{23} on Take-off Distances

3.2 SIZING TO TAKE-OFF DISTANCE REQUIREMENTS

Take-off distances of airplanes are determined by the following factors:

1. Take-off weight, W_{TO}

2. Take-off speed, V_{TO} (also called lift-off speed)

3. Thrust-to-weight ratio at take-off, $(T/W)_{TO}$ (or weight-to-power ratio, $(W/P)_{TO}$ and the corresponding propeller characteristics)

4. Aerodynamic drag coefficient, C_{D_G} and ground friction coefficient, μ_G

5. Pilot technique

In this section it will be assumed, that take-offs take place from hardened surfaces (concrete or asphalt) unless otherwise stated.

Take-off requirements are normally given in terms of take-off field length requirements. These requirements differ widely and depend on the type of airplane under consideration.

For civil airplanes, the requirements of FAR 23 and FAR 25 must be adhered to. In the case of homebuilt airplanes it is not necessary to design to the FAR's. In that case, the individual designer may set his own take-off requirements.

For military airplanes the requirements are usually set forth in the so-called Request-for-Proposal or RFP. All take-off calculations for military airplanes must be done with the definitions of Reference 15.

Depending on the type of mission, the take-off requirements are frequently spelled out in terms of minimum ground run requirements in combination with some minimum climb capability. For Navy airplanes with carrier capability, the limitations of the catapult system on the carrier must be accounted for.

Sub-sections (3.2.1) through (3.2.6) address the sizing to take-off requirements for airplanes with essentially mechanical flap systems. For airplanes with 'augmented' flaps systems or for vectored thrust airplanes the reader should consult Refs. 12 and 13.

3.2.1 Sizing to FAR 23 Take-off Distance Requirements

Figure 3.2 presents a definition of take-off distances used in the process of sizing an airplane to FAR 23 requirements. FAR 23 airplanes usually are propeller driven airplanes.

In Reference 11 it is shown, that the take-off ground run, s_{TOG} of an airplane is proportional to take-off wing loading $(W/S)_{TO}$, take-off power loading, $(W/P)_{TO}$ and to the maximum take-off lift coefficient, $C_{L_{max_{TO}}}$:

$$s_{TOG} \propto (W/S)_{TO}(W/P)_{TO}/\sigma C_{L_{max_{TO}}} = TOP_{23}, \qquad (3.2)$$

where TOP_{23} is the so-called take-off parameter for FAR 23 airplanes. Its dimension is $lbs^2/ft^2 hp$.

The reader should keep in mind, that the lift coefficient at lift-off, $C_{L_{TO}}$ is related to the maximum take-off lift coefficient, $C_{L_{max_{TO}}}$ by:

$$C_{L_{TO}} = C_{L_{max_{TO}}}/1.21 \qquad (3.3)$$

Figure 3.3 relates s_{TOG} to the take off parameter, TOP_{23} for a range of single and twin engine FAR 23 certified airplanes. Figure 3.4 relates s_{TO} and s_{TOG} to each other. It is seen that there is a lot of scatter in the data. One reason is, that take-off procedures vary widely. Another is that take-off thrust depends strongly on propeller characteristics. Finally, take-off rotation to lift-off attitude depends on control power, control feel and on airplane inertia. Nevertheless, it is useful to employ the correlation lines of Figures 3.3 and 3.4 in the preliminary sizing process. The correlation lines drawn suggest the following relationships:

$$s_{TOG} = 4.9 TOP_{23} + 0.009 TOP_{23}^2 \qquad (3.4)$$

and, since Figure 3.4 implies:

$$s_{TO} = 1.66 s_{TOG} \qquad (3.5)$$

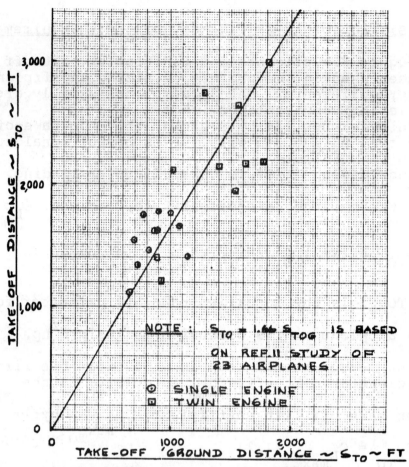

Figure 3.4 Correlation of Ground Distance and Total
Distance for Take-off (FAR 23)

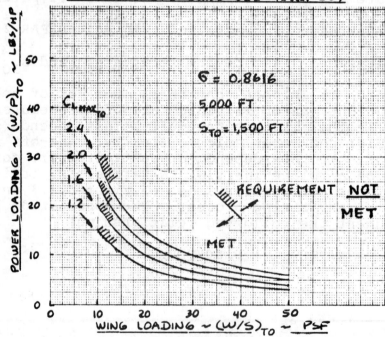

Figure 3.5 Effect of Take-off Wing Loading and Maximum
Take-off Lift Coefficient on Take-off Power
Loading

it follows that:

$$s_{TO} = 8.134 TOP_{23} + 0.0149 TOP_{23}^2 \qquad (3.6)$$

The assumption was made that FAR 23 airplanes are nearly always propeller driven airplanes. For jet airplanes the parameter W/P in Eqn.(3.2) should be replaced by W/T. The reader is advised to use the sizing procedure of 3.2.3 for FAR 23 jet airplanes.

An example of FAR 23 take-off sizing will now be discussed.

3.2.2 Example of FAR 23 Take-off Distance Sizing

Assume that it is required to size a propeller-driven airplane to the following take-off criteria:

$s_{TOG} < 1,000$ ft and $s_{TO} < 1,500$ ft at an altitude of 5,000 ft in standard atmosphere.

Since Eqn.(3.5) stipulates that s_{TOG} and s_{TO} are related to each other, the first requirement translates into:

$s_{TO} < 1,660$ ft.

This clearly violates the second requirement. Therefore the second requirement dominates. From Eqn.(3.5) it follows that for both take-off requirements to be met, it is necessary that:

$$1,500 = 8.134 TOP_{23} + 0.0149 TOP_{23}^2$$

From this in turn it follows that:

$$TOP_{23} = 145.6 \ lbs^2/ft^2 hp$$

Since $\sigma = 0.8616$ at 5,000 ft, this result when combined with Eqn.(3.2) translates into:

$$(W/S)_{TO}(W/P)_{TO}/C_{L_{max_{TO}}} < 145.6 \times 0.8616 = 125.4 \ lbs^2/ft^2 hp$$

The following tabulation can now be made for the required values of $(W/P)_{TO}$:

$$(W/S)_{TO} \quad C_{L_{max_{TO}}} \quad = \quad 1.2 \quad\quad 1.6 \quad\quad 2.0 \quad\quad 2.4$$

psf

10	$(W/P)_{TO}$ =	15.0	20.1	25.1	30.1
30		5.0	6.7	8.4	10.0
50		3.0	4.0	5.0	6.0

Figure 3.5 translates this tabulation into regions of $(W/S)_{TO}$ and $(W/P)_{TO}$ for given values of $C_{L_{max_{TO}}}$

so that the take-off distance requirement is satisfied.

3.2.3 Sizing to FAR 25 Take-off Distance Requirements

Figure 3.6 defines those quantities important to FAR 25 take-off field length requirements.

In Reference 11 it is shown that the take-off field length, s_{TOFL} is proportional to take-off wing loading, $(W/S)_{TO}$, take-off thrust-to-weight ratio, $(T/W)_{TO}$ and to maximum take-off lift coefficient, $C_{L_{max_{TO}}}$:

$$s_{TOFL} \propto (W/S)_{TO}/\{\sigma C_{L_{max_{TO}}}(T/W)_{TO}\} = TOP_{25}, \qquad (3.7)$$

where TOP_{25} is the take-off parameter for FAR 25 certified airplanes. Its dimension is lbs/ft^2.

Figure 3.7 shows that the relationship expressed by Eqn.(3.7) can be written as:

$$s_{TOFL} = 37.5(W/S)_{TO}/\{\sigma C_{L_{max_{TO}}}(T/W)_{TO}\} = 37.5TOP_{25} \qquad (3.8)$$

Typical values for $C_{L_{max_{TO}}}$ can be found in Table 3.1.

FAR 25 certified airplanes can be both jet-driven or propeller-driven (for example prop-fans or turboprops). In the case of propeller-driven airplanes it is necessary to convert the value of T/W required in take-off to the corresponding value of W/P. Figure 3.8 shows how this can be done, depending on the assumed propeller characteristics.

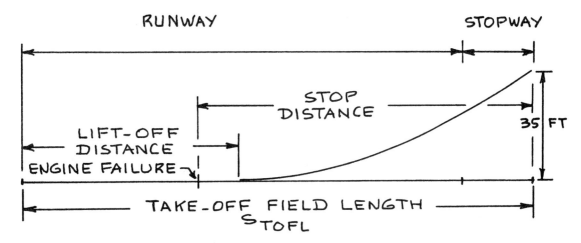

Figure 3.6 Definition of FAR 25 Take-off Distances

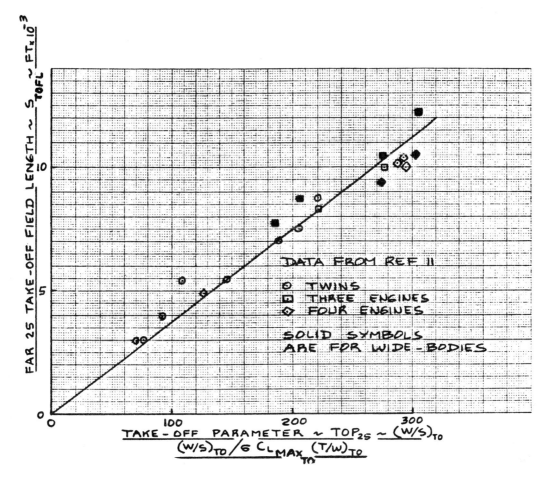

Figure 3.7 Effect of Take-off Parameter, TOP_{25} on
FAR 25 Take-off Field Length

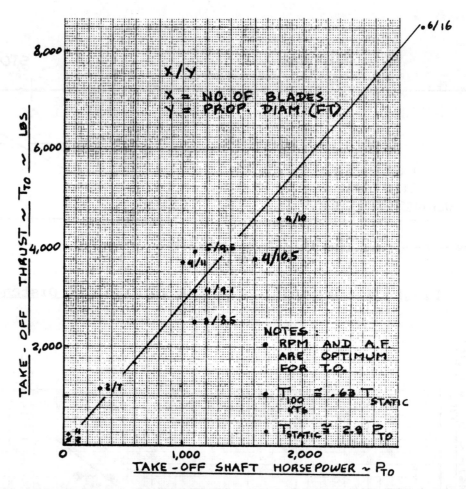

Figure 3.8 Effect of Shaft Horsepower on Take-off Thrust

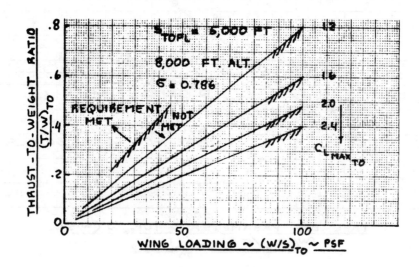

Figure 3.9 Effect of Take-off Wing Loading and Maximum
Take-off Lift Coefficient on Take-off Thrust-
to-Weight Ratio

3.2.4 Example of FAR 25 Take-off Distance Sizing

It is required to size a passenger airplane so that the FAR 25 fieldlength is given by:

s_{TOFL} < 5,000 ft at 8,000 ft standard atmosphere

From Eqn.(3.8) it is seen, that the fieldlength requirement will be satisfied as long as:

TOP_{25} = 5,000/37.5 = 133.3 lbs/ft^2

At 8,000 ft, σ = 0.786. Therefore with Eqn.(3.7):

$(W/S)_{TO}/\{C_{L_{max_{TO}}}(T/W)_{TO}\}$ = 133.3x0.786 = 104.8 lbs/ft^2

The following tabulation can now be made for the required values of $(T/W)_{TO}$:

$(W/S)_{TO}$ psf	$C_{L_{max_{TO}}}$ =	1.2	1.6	2.0	2.4
40	$(T/W)_{TO}$ =	0.32	0.24	0.19	0.16
60		0.48	0.36	0.29	0.24
80		0.64	0.48	0.38	0.32
100		0.80	0.60	0.48	0.40

Figure 3.9 illustrates the range of values of $(W/S)_{TO}$, $(T/W)_{TO}$ and $C_{L_{max_{TO}}}$ for which the

fieldlength requirement is satisfied.

3.2.5 Sizing to Military Take-off Distance Requirements

3.2.5.1 Land based airplanes

Reference 15 defines the military take-off field length as that in Figure 3.6 except for the obstacle height, which is 50 ft instead of 35 ft.

Military take-off requirements are frequently specified in terms of maximum allowable groundrun, s_{TOG}.

The groundrun may be estimated from:

$$s_{TOG} = \frac{k_1 (W/S)_{TO}}{\rho [C_{L_{max_{TO}}} \{k_2 (X/W)_{TO} - \mu_G\} - 0.72 C_{D_o}]} \qquad (3.9)$$

This equation is a variation of Eqn.(5-75) in Ref.16. It assumes that the following conditions prevail:

a. no wind
b. level runway

The quantities k_1, k_2 and X, are defined as follows:

for jets:	for props:
$X = T$	$X = P$
$k_1 = 0.0447$	$k_1 = 0.0376$
$k_2 = 0.75\dfrac{(5 + \lambda)}{(4 + \lambda)}$	$k_2 = l_p (\sigma N D_p^2 / P_{TO})^{1/3}$
λ = engine bypass ratio	for constant speed props: $l_p = 5.75$
	for fixed pitch props: $l_p = 4.60$

The term $P_{TO}/N D_p^2$ is the propeller disk loading.

Note, that P_{TO} stands for the total take-off power with

all engines operating. N is the number of engines. Typical values for propeller disk loading can be deduced from the data in Ref.9. Lacking such data it is suggested to use the following ranges:

Typical Propeller Disk Loadings in hp/ft^2

Singles	Light Twins	Heavy Twins	Turboprops
3-8	6-10	8-14	10-30

Equation (3.9) applies whenever power or thrust effects on lift can be neglected. If this is not the case the reader is referred to Refs. 12 and 13.

Table 3.2 gives typical values for the ground friction coefficient, μ_G for different surfaces.

Table 3.2 Ground Friction Coefficient, μ_G
===

Surface Type	μ_G	
Concrete	0.02 - 0.03	(0.025 per Ref.15)
Asphalt	0.02 - 0.03	
Hard Turf	0.05	
Short Grass	0.05	
Long Grass	0.10	
Soft Ground	0.10 - 0.30	

3.2.5.2 Carrier based airplanes

For carrier based airplanes, the limitations of the catapult system need to be accounted for. These limitations are usually stated in terms of relations between take-off weight and launch speed at the end of the catapult, V_{cat}. Figure 3.10 provides some data for existing catapult systems used by the USNavy.

At the end of the catapult stroke, the following relationship must be satisfied:

$$0.5\rho(V_{wod} + V_{cat})^2 S C_{L_{max_{TO}}} /1.21 = W_{TO} \qquad (3.10)$$

From Eqn.(3.10) it is possible to determine the range of values for W/S, T/W and $C_{L_{max_{TO}}}$ which ensure staying within catapult capabilities.

3.2.6 Example of Sizing to Military Take-off Distance Requirements

It is required to size a Navy attack airplane such that:

a) for land based take-offs: $s_{TOG} < 2,500$ ft at sealevel, standard atmosphere, concrete runways.

b) for carrier take-offs: with V_{wod} = 25 kts the airplane is to be compatible with the Mark C13 catapult system.

Figure 3.11 shows the range of values of W_{TO}/S,

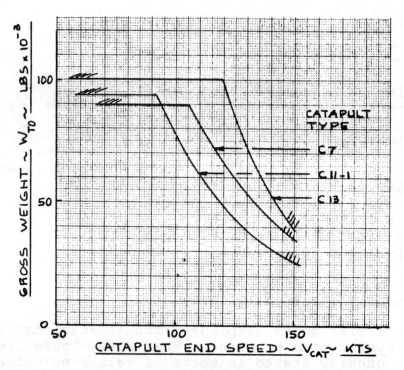

Figure 3.10 Effect of Take-off Weight on Catapult End
Speed for Three Types of Catapult

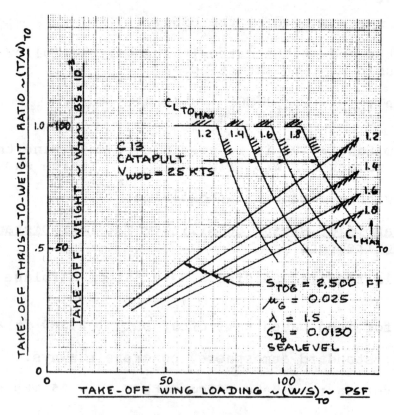

Figure 3.11 Effect of Maximum Take-off Lift Coefficient
and Catapult Limitations on Weight, Wing
Loading and Thrust-to-Weight Ratio at
Take-off

$(T/W)_{TO}$ and $C_{L_{max_{TO}}}$, which satisfy the land based

groundrun requirement for μ_G = 0.025, for an assumed

bypass ratio of λ = 1.5 and for an assumed zero-lift drag
coefficient of C_{D_0} = 0.0130.

The C13 catapult data of Figure 3.10 indicate that
W_{TO} < 100,000 lbs must always be satisfied. Below that

weight, Figure 3.10 shows the following relationship
between weight and catapult speed:

Take-off Weight, W_{TO} (lbs)	Catapult Speed, V_{cat} (kts)
100,000	120
72,000	130
53,000	140
39,000	150

Eqn.(3.10) can be used to relate values of take-off
weight, W_{TO} to allowable take-off wing loadings, $(W/S)_{TO}$

for different take-off lift coefficients, $C_{L_{max_{TO}}}$.

Figure 3.11 shows the results for a WOD of 25 kts.

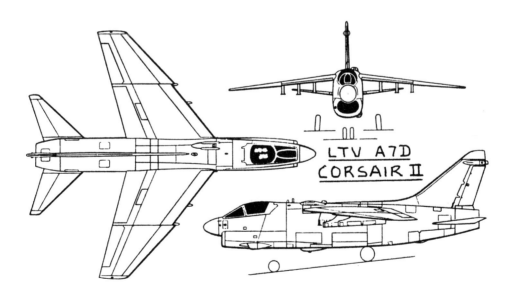

3.3. SIZING TO LANDING DISTANCE REQUIREMENTS

Landing distances of airplanes are determined by five factors:

1. Landing Weight, W_L

2. Approach speed, V_A

3. Deceleration method used

4. Flying qualities of the airplane

5. Pilot technique

Landing distance requirements are nearly always formulated at the design landing weight, W_L of an airplane. Table 3.3 shows how W_L is related to W_{TO} for twelve types of airplanes.

Kinetic energy considerations suggest that the approach speed should have a 'square' effect on the total landing distance. After an airplane has touched down, the following deceleration methods can be used:

a. Brakes
b. Thrust reversers
c. Parachutes
d. Arresting systems (field-based or carrier-based)
e. Crash barriers

Data presented in this section are based on existing industry practice in decelerating airplanes after touchdown.

For civil airplanes, the requirements of FAR 23 and FAR 25 are in force. In the case of homebuilt airplanes, it is not necessary to design to FAR landing distance requirements.

For military airplanes the requirements are usually laid down in the RFP. Ground runs are sometimes specified without their accompanying air distances.

In the case of Navy airplanes the capabilities of the on deck arresting system need to be taken into consideration.

Table 3.3 Typical Values For Landing Weight to Take-off Weight Ratio

$$W_L/W_{TO}$$

Airplane Type	Minimum	Average	Maximum
1. Homebuilts	0.96	1.0	1.0
2. Single Engine Propeller Driven	0.95	0.997	1.0
3. Twin Engine Propeller Driven	0.88	0.99	1.0
4. Agricultural	0.7	0.94	1.0
5. Business Jets	0.69	0.88	0.96
6. Regional TBP	0.92	0.98	1.0
7. Transport Jets	0.65	0.84	1.0
8. Military Trainers	0.87	0.99	1.1
9. Fighters (jets)	0.78	insufficient	1.0
(tbp's)	0.57	data	1.0
10. Mil. Patrol, Bomb and Transports (jets)	0.68	0.76	0.83
(tbp's)	0.77	0.84	1.0
11. Flying Boats, Amphibious and Float Airplanes			
(land)	0.79	insufficient	0.95
(water)	0.98	data	1.0
12. Supersonic Cruise Airplanes	0.63	0.75	0.88

Note: These data are based on Tables 2.3 through 2.14.

Sub-sections 3.3.1 through 3.3.6 address the sizing to landing requirements for airplanes with essentially mechanical flap systems. For airplanes with 'augmented' flaps or for vectored thrust airplanes the reader should consult Refs. 12 and 13.

3.3.1 Sizing to FAR 23 Landing Distance Requirements

Figure 3.12 presents a definition of landing distances used in the process of sizing an airplane to FAR 23 requirements.

The reader should note that the approach speed is specified as:

$$V_A = 1.3V_{s_L} \hspace{4cm} (3.11)$$

Figure 3.13 shows how the landing ground run, s_{LG} is related to the square of the stall speed, V_{s_L}. The stall speed here is that in the landing configuration: gear down, landing flaps and power-off.

The data in Figure 3.13 suggest the following relation:

$$s_{LG} = 0.265V_{s_L}^2 \hspace{4cm} (3.12)$$

Note, that the distance is in ft and the stall speed is in kts.

Figure 3.14 shows how the total landing distance, s_L is related to s_{LG}. This figure suggests the following relationship:

$$s_L = 1.938s_{LG} \hspace{4cm} (3.13)$$

By specifying the maximum allowable total landing distance, s_L, it is possible to find the corresponding landing groundrun, s_{LG}. From the latter the maximum allowable stall speed can be found. It was already shown in section 3.1 that this in turn can be translated into a relation between wing-loading $(W/S)_L$ and $C_{L_{max_L}}$.

It is often useful to combine Eqns.(3.12) and (3.13) into:

$$s_L = 0.5136V_{s_L}^2 \hspace{4cm} (3.14)$$

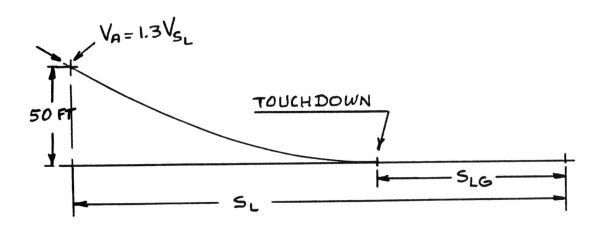

Figure 3.12 Definition of FAR 23 Landing Distances

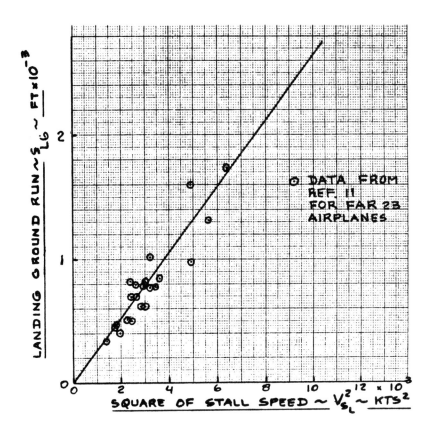

Figure 3.13 Effect of Square of Stall Speed on Landing
Groundrun

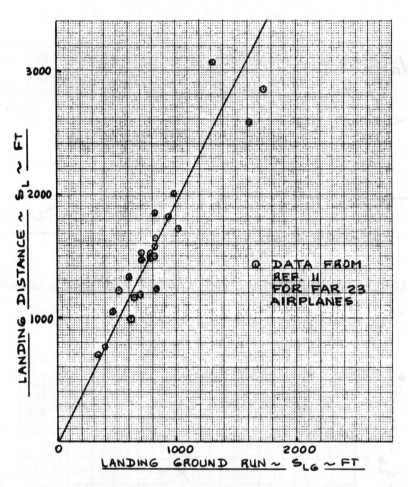

Figure 3.14 Correlation Between Groundrun and Landing
Distance

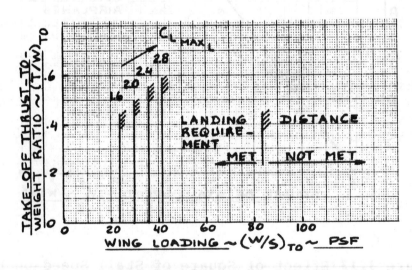

Figure 3.15 Allowable Wing Loadings to Meet a Landing
Distance Requirement

3.3.2 Example of FAR 23 Landing Distance Sizing

It is required to size a propeller driven twin to a landing field length of 2,500 ft. at 5,000 ft altitude. The design landing weight is specified as: $W_L = 0.95W_{TO}$.

From Eqn.(3.14) it follows that:

$$V_{s_L} = \{2,500/0.5136\}^{1/2} = 69.8 \text{ kts}$$

With the help of Eqn.(3.1) this translates into the following requirement:

$$2(W/S)_L/0.002049C_{L_{max_L}} = (69.8 \times 1.688)^2 = 13,869 \text{ ft}^2/\text{sec}^2$$

From this it follows that:

$$(W/S)_L = 14.2C_{L_{max_L}}$$

With $W_L = 0.95W_{TO}$, this yields:

$$(W/S)_{TO} = 14.9C_{L_{max_L}}$$

Figure 3.15 presents the range of values of $(W/S)_{TO}$ and $C_{L_{max_L}}$ which meet the landing distance requirement.

3.3.3 Sizing to FAR 23 Landing Distance Requirements

Figure 3.16 defines the quantities which are important in the FAR 25 field length requirements.

The FAR landing field length is defined as the total landing distance (Figure 3.16) divided by 0.6. This factor of safety is included to account for variations in pilot technique and other conditions beyond the control of FAA.

Note that the approach speed is always defined as:

$$V_A = 1.3V_{s_L} \tag{3.15}$$

Figure 3.17 relates the FAR field length to V_A^2:

$$s_{FL} = 0.3V_A^2, \tag{3.16}$$

where s_{FL} is in ft and V_A is in kts.

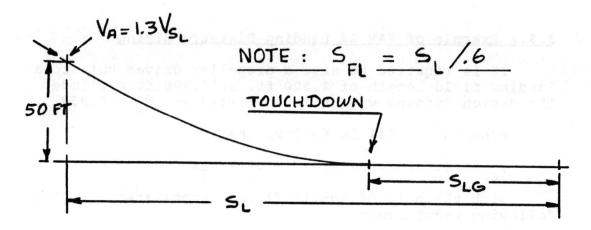

Figure 3.16 Definition of FAR 25 Landing Distances

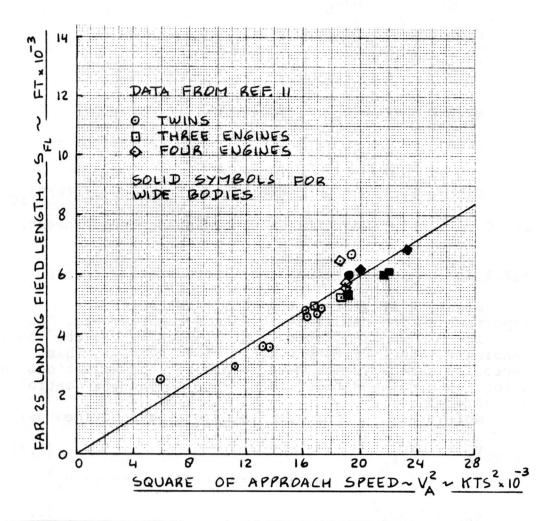

Figure 3.17 Effect of Square of Approach Speed on
FAR 25 Field Length

With the help of Eqn.(3.1) and a requirement for a maximum acceptable landing field length it is again possible to relate $(W/S)_L$ (and thus $(W/S)_{TO}$) to $C_{L_{max_L}}$.

The reader will have observed that under FAR 23 the fieldlength is correlated with V_{s_L} while under FAR 25 it is correlated with V_A. The reason is that data available in the literature (such as Ref.9) tends to be presented in such a way as to force this type of correlation.

3.3.4 Example of FAR 25 Landing Distance Sizing

It is required to size a jet transport for a landing field length of 5,000 ft at sealevel on a standard day. It may be assumed, that: $W_L = 0.85W_{TO}$.

From Eqn.(3.16) it follows that:

$$V_A = (5,000/0.3)^{1/2} = 129.1 \text{ kts}$$

With Eqn.(3.15):

$$V_{s_L} = 129.1/1.3 = 99.3 \text{ kts.}$$

With Eqn.(3.1) this in turn yields:

$$2(W/S)_L/0.002378C_{L_{max_L}} = (99.3\text{x}1.688)^2 = 28,100 \text{ ft}^2/\text{sec}^2$$

Therefore:

$$(W/S)_L = 33.4C_{L_{max_L}}, \text{ so that:}$$

$$(W/S)_{TO} = (33.4/0.85)C_{L_{max_L}} = 39.3C_{L_{max_L}}$$

Figure 3.18 illustrates how $(W/S)_{TO}$ and $C_{L_{max_L}}$ are

related to satisfy the stated field length requirement.

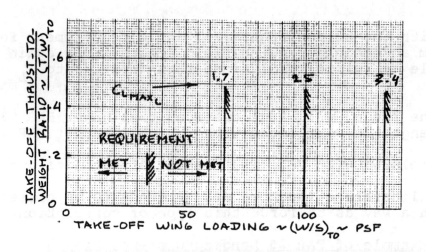

Figure 3.18 Allowable Wing Loadings to Meet a Field
Length Requirement

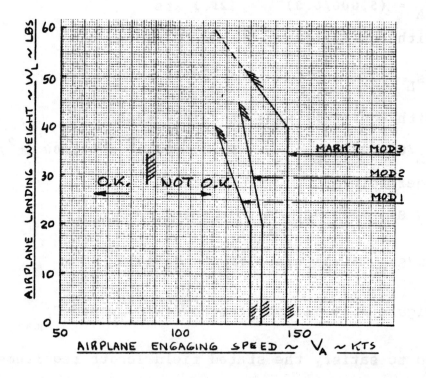

Figure 3.19 Performance Limitations of Three Types
of Arresting Gears

3.3.5 Sizing to Military Landing Distance Requirements

3.3.5.1 Land based airplanes

Military requirements for landing distances are normally defined in the RFP. The sizing methods for FAR 25 can be employed with one proviso: military approach speeds are usually less than those of commercial airplanes. From Reference 15:

$$V_A = 1.2 V_{s_L} \tag{3.17}$$

The effect of this is to decrease the landing distance by the square of the approach speed ratio.

3.3.5.2 Carrier based airplanes

For carrier based airplanes, the approach speed is usually given by:

$$V_A = 1.1 V_{s_{PA}} \tag{3.18}$$

In addition, the limitations of the arresting system need to be accounted for. Figure 3.19 illustrates typical arresting gear limitations.

3.3.6 Example of Sizing to Military Landing Distance Requirements

For the same Navy attack airplane of Sub-section 3.2.6, it is requested to perform the sizing to landing requirements such that:

a) for shore based landings: s_{FL} = 3,500 ft at sea-level, standard atmosphere, concrete runways.

b) for carrier landings the airplane is to be compatible with the Mark7 Mod3 arresting gear.

c) landing weight, W_L is equal to 0.80 times the take-off weight, W_{TO}

First item a) will be discussed. The FAR 25 data of Figure 3.17 are used to establish the fact, that for a fieldlength of s_{FL} = 3,500 ft, the corresponding approach speed is $(11,800)^{1/2}$ = 108.6 kts.

However, for military airplanes this implies an approach stall speed of 108.6/1.2 = 90.5 kts.

From Eqn.(3.1) it now follows that:

$$\{2(W/S)_L\}/(0.002378C_{L_{max_L}}) = (90.5 \times 1.688)^2 =$$

$$= 23,337 \text{ ft}^2/\text{sec}^2$$

Therefore:

$$(W/S)_L = 27.7C_{L_{max_L}}$$

From item c) it follows that:

$$(W/S)_{TO} = 34.7C_{L_{max_L}}$$

Figure 3.20 shows the allowable wing loadings at take-off, to meet this landing requirement.

To satisfy item b), it is observed from Figure 3.19 that for the Mark7 Mod3 arresting gear, V_A = 145 kts, as long as the landing weight is under 40,000 lbs. That implies a take-off weight of less than 50,000 lbs.

From Eqn.(3.18) it follows that:

$$V_{s_{PA}} = 145/1.15 = 126.1 \text{ kts}$$

With Eqn.(3.1) this in turn yields:

$$(W/S)_A = 0.5 \times 0.002378 \times (126.1 \times 1.688)^2 \times C_{L_{max_{PA}}} =$$

$$= 53.9C_{L_{max_{PA}}}$$

This implies a take-off wing loading of:

$$(W/S)_{TO} = (53.9/0.8)C_{L_{max_{PA}}} = 67.3C_{L_{max_{PA}}}$$

Figure 3.20 shows how this requirement compares with the shore based field length requirement. It is seen that at least in this example, the latter is the more critical.

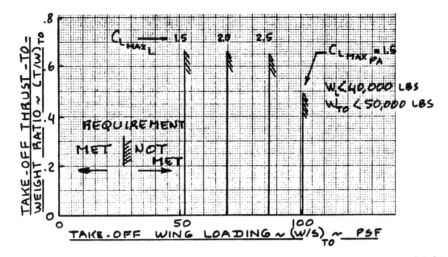

Figure 3.20 Allowable Wing Loadings to meet Military
Field and Carrier Landing Requirements

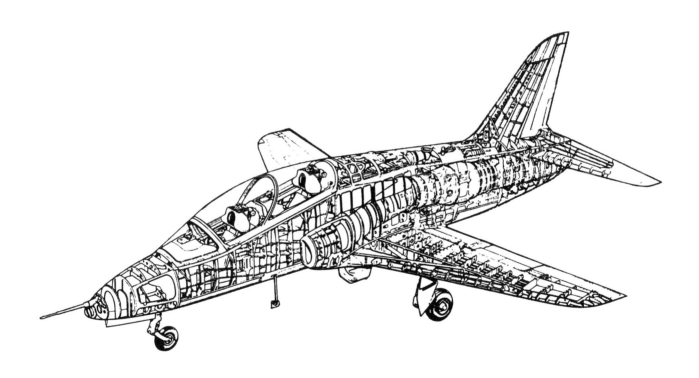

BRITISH AEROSPACE HAWK

3.4 SIZING TO CLIMB REQUIREMENTS

All airplanes must meet certain climb rate or climb gradient requirements. To size an airplane for climb requirements, it is necessary to have an estimate for the airplane drag polar. Sub-section 3.4.1 presents a rapid method for estimating drag polars for low speed flight conditions. Sub-section 3.4.2 applies this method to an example airplane.

For civil airplanes, the climb requirements of either FAR 23 or FAR 25 must be met. Sub-sections 3.4.3 and 3.4.6 summarize these requirements. Sub-sections 3.4.4 and 3.4.7 present rapid methods for sizing airplanes to these requirements. Example applications are presented in Sub-sections 3.4.5 and 3.4.8.

For military airplanes either the requirements of Reference 15 or, whatever climb requirements are specified in the RFP must be met. The military climb requirements of Reference 15 are summarized in Sub-section 3.4.9.

The methods of Sub-sections 3.4.3 and 3.4.6 can also be used to size military airplanes to low speed climb requirements. For sizing to: very high climb rates, time-to-climb to altitude and ceiling requirements, the reader is referred to Sub-section 3.4.10. Sizing to specific excess power requirements is discussed in Sub-section 3.4.11. An application of these military requirements is presented in Sub-section 3.4.12.

3.4.1 A Method for Estimating Drag Polars at Low Speed

Assuming a parabolic drag polar, the drag coefficient of an airplane can be written as:

$$C_D = C_{D_0} + C_L^2/\pi Ae \qquad (3.19)$$

The zero-lift drag coefficient, C_{D_0} can be expressed as:

$$C_{D_0} = f/S, \qquad (3.20)$$

where f is the equivalent parasite area and S is the wing area.

It is possible to relate equivalent parasite area, f to wetted area S_{wet}. This is shown in Figures (3.21a and b).

It is possible to represent Figures (3.21) with the following empirically obtained equation:

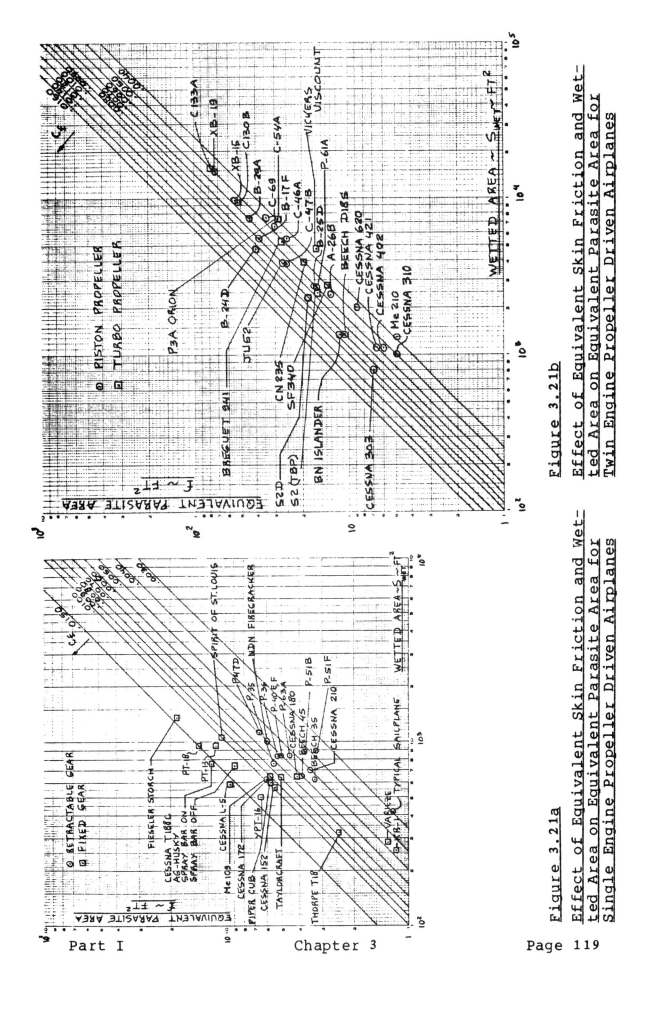

Figure 3.21b

Effect of Equivalent Skin Friction and Wetted Area on Equivalent Parasite Area for
Twin Engine Propeller Driven Airplanes

Figure 3.21a

Effect of Equivalent Skin Friction and Wetted Area on Equivalent Parasite Area for
Single Engine Propeller Driven Airplanes

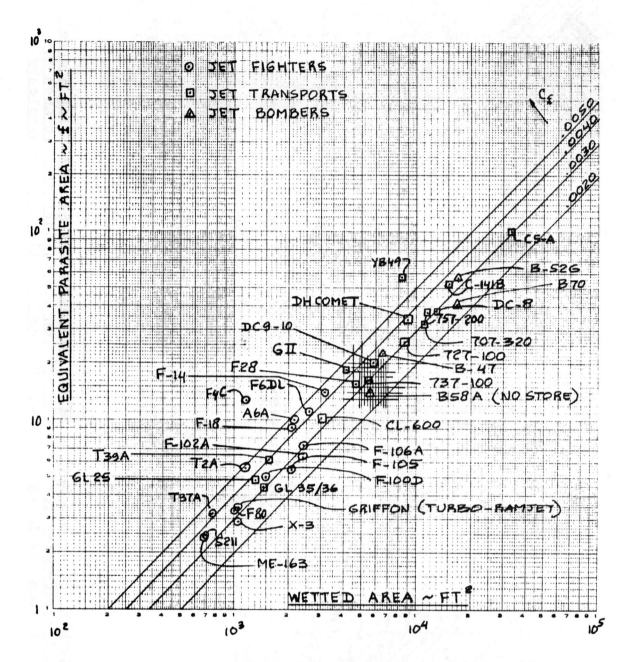

Figure 3.21c Effect of Equivalent Skin Friction and Wetted Area on Equivalent Parasite Area for
Jets: Fighters, Bombers and Transports

$$\log_{10}f = a + b\log_{10}S_{wet} \qquad (3.21)$$

The correlation coefficients a and b are themselves a function of the equivalent skin friction coefficient of an airplane, c_f. The latter is determined by the

smoothness and streamlining designed into the airplane. Table (3.4) shows typical values for a and for b for a range of c_f- values. Figures (3.21) in turn allow the

reader to quickly estimate a realistic value for c_f.

It is evident, that the method for estimating drag boils down to the ability to predict a realistic value for S_{wet}. It turns out, that S_{wet} correlates well with

W_{TO} for a wide range of airplanes. Figures (3.22a-d)

show this. The scatter in these figures is mainly due to differences in wing loading, cabin sizes and nacelle design. Most airplanes fall in the ten percent band.

With the help of Figures 3.22 it is possible to obtain an initial estimate for airplane wetted area without knowing what the airplanes actually looks like.

Figures (3.22) also imply the following:

$$\log_{10}S_{wet} = c + d\log_{10}W_{TO} \qquad (3.22)$$

The constants c and d are regression line coefficients. Values for c and d were obtained by correlating wetted area and take-off weight data for 230 airplanes. These airplanes were categorized in the same types used in Chapter 2. Table 3.5 lists the values of the regression line coefficients c and d for twelve types of airplanes.

Since an estimate for W_{TO} was already obtained in

Chapter 2, the drag polar for the clean airplane can now be determined.

For take-off and for landing, the effect of flaps and of the landing gear need to be accounted for. The additional zero-lift drag coefficients due to flaps and due to landing gear are strongly dependent on the size and type of these items.

Typical values for ΔC_{D_0} are given in Table 3.6.

Table 3.4 Correlation Coefficients for Parasite Area
===
Versus Wetted Area (Eqn.(3.21))
===================================

Equivalent Skin Friction Coefficient, c_f	a	b
0.0090	-2.0458	1.0000
0.0080	-2.0969	1.0000
0.0070	-2.1549	1.0000
0.0060	-2.2218	1.0000
0.0050	-2.3010	1.0000
0.0040	-2.3979	1.0000
0.0030	-2.5229	1.0000
0.0020	-2.6990	1.0000

Table 3.5 Regression Line Coefficients for Take-off
===
Weight Versus Wetted Area (Eqn.(3.22))
=======================================

Airplane Type	c	d
1. Homebuilts	1.2362	0.4319
2. Single Engine Propeller Driven	1.0892	0.5147
3. Twin Engine Propeller Driven	0.8635	0.5632
4. Agricultural	1.0447	0.5326
5. Business Jets	0.2263	0.6977
6. Regional Turboprops	-0.0866	0.8099
7. Transport Jets	0.0199	0.7531
8. Military Trainers*	0.8565	0.5423
9. Fighters*	-0.1289	0.7506
10. Mil. Patrol, Bomb and Transport	0.1628	0.7316
11. Flying Boats, Amph. and Float	0.6295	0.6708
12. Supersonic Cruise Airplanes	-1.1868	0.9609

* For these airplanes, wetted areas were correlated with 'clean', maximum take-off weights. No stores were accounted for.

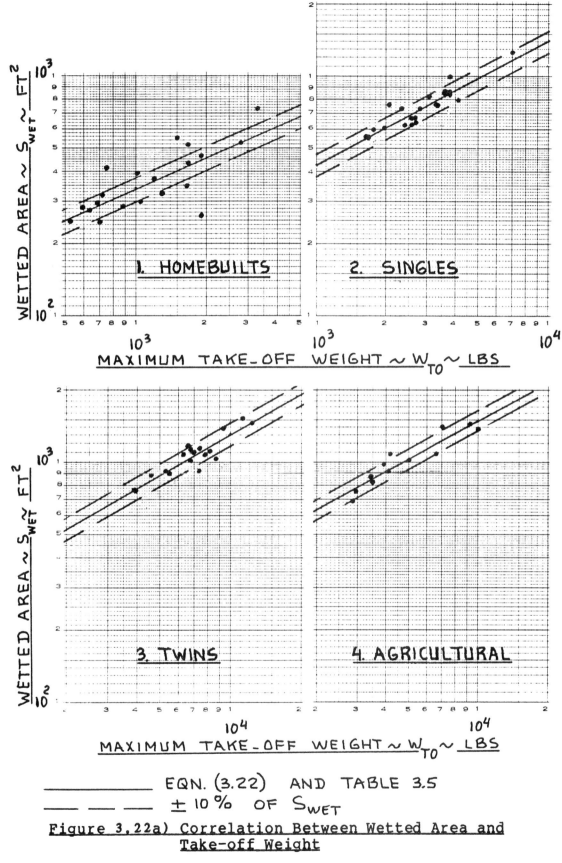

EQN. (3.22)   AND TABLE 3.5

±10% OF S$_{WET}$

Figure 3.22a) Correlation Between Wetted Area and
Take-off Weight

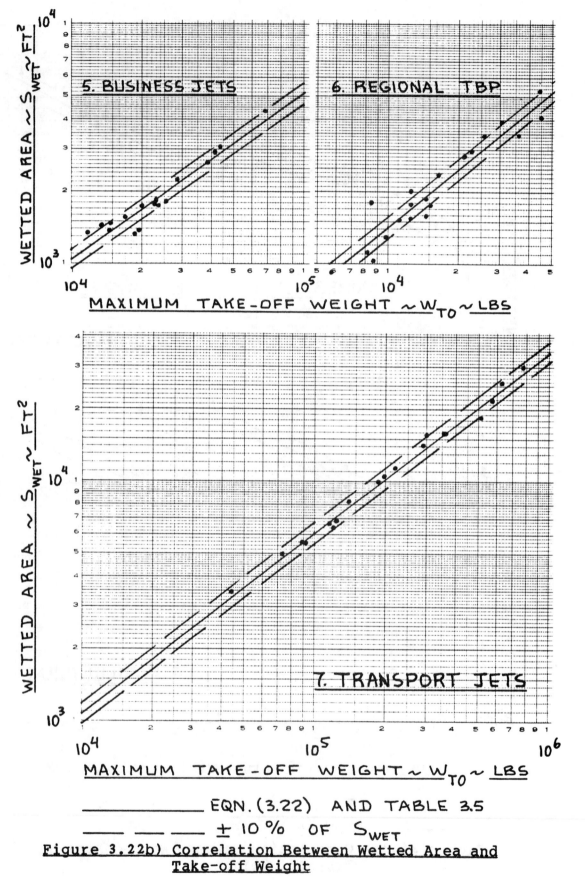

EQN.(3.22) AND TABLE 3.5

± 10% OF S_{WET}

Figure 3.22b) Correlation Between Wetted Area and Take-off Weight

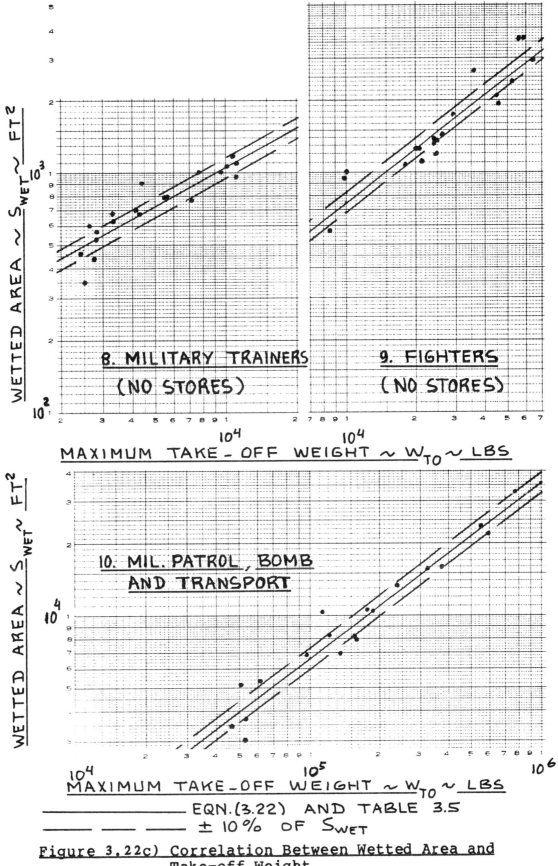

WETTED AREA ~ S_{WET} ~ FT^2

8. MILITARY TRAINERS
(NO STORES)

9. FIGHTERS
(NO STORES)

MAXIMUM TAKE-OFF WEIGHT ~ W_{TO} ~ LBS

10. MIL. PATROL, BOMB
AND TRANSPORT

WETTED AREA ~ S_{WET} ~ FT^2

MAXIMUM TAKE-OFF WEIGHT ~ W_{TO} ~ LBS

————————————— EQN.(3.22) AND TABLE 3.5
——— ——— ——— ± 10% OF S_{WET}

Figure 3.22c) Correlation Between Wetted Area and
Take-off Weight

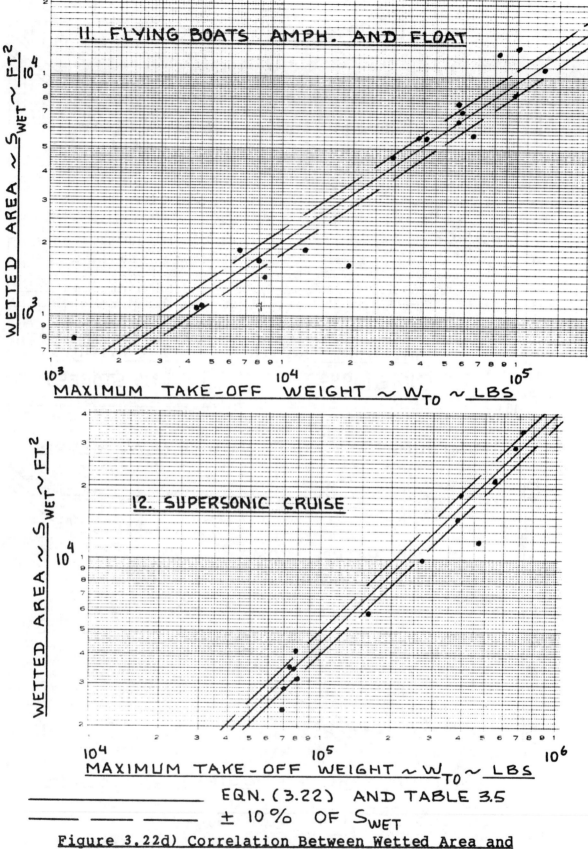

11. FLYING BOATS AMPH. AND FLOAT

WETTED AREA $\sim S_{WET} \sim FT^2$

MAXIMUM TAKE-OFF WEIGHT $\sim W_{TO} \sim LBS$

12. SUPERSONIC CRUISE

WETTED AREA $\sim S_{WET} \sim FT^2$

MAXIMUM TAKE-OFF WEIGHT $\sim W_{TO} \sim LBS$

——————————— EQN. (3.22) AND TABLE 3.5

— — — — — — $\pm$ 10 % OF S_{WET}

Figure 3.22d) Correlation Between Wetted Area and Take-off Weight

Table 3.6 First Estimates for ΔC_{D_0} and 'e'
===
With Flaps and Gear Down
==========================

Configuration	ΔC_{D_0}	e
Clean	0	0.80 - 0.85
Take-off flaps	0.010 - 0.020	0.75 - 0.80
Landing Flaps	0.055 - 0.075	0.70 - 0.75
Landing Gear	0.015 - 0.025	no effect

Which values are selected depends on flap and gear type. Split flaps are more 'draggy' than Fowler flaps. Full span flaps are more 'draggy' than partial span flaps. Wing mounted landing gears on high wing airplanes are more 'draggy' than those on low wing airplanes. Reference 5 provides detailed information on how to estimate these drag items.

3.4.2 Example of Drag Polar Determination

It is required to find the clean, take-off and landing drag polars for a jet airplane with W_{TO}= 10,000 lbs.

Figure (3.22), or Eqn.(3.22) shows that for this airplane, S_{wet}= 1,050 ft^2. From Figure (3.21) it is apparent, that a c_f value of 0.0030 is reasonable. The reader is asked to show, that use of Eqn.(3.21) gives the same result. From Figure (3.21) or from Eqn.(3.21) it now follows that:

$$f = 3.15 \text{ ft}^2.$$

For a jet airplane in this category, typical wing loadings will range from 50 psf to 100 psf. It will be assumed, that an average wing loading for this category airplane is 75 psf. With the weight of W_{TO} = 10,000 lbs, the following data are now obtained:

W_{TO}	$(W/S)_{TO}$	S	S_{wet}	f	C_{D_0}
10,000	75	133	1,050	3.15	0.0237

The reader will note, that when wing area is varied at constant weight, the wetted area will change.

If it is now assumed, that A = 10 and e = 0.85 then it is possible to find the 'clean' drag polars at low speed as:

$$C_D = 0.0237 + 0.0374 C_L^2$$

The additional zero-lift drag coefficients due to flaps and due to gear are assumed from Sub-section 3.4.1 as:

ΔC_{D_0} due to:

take-off flaps = 0.015, with e = 0.8

landing flaps = 0.060, with e = 0.75

Landing gear = 0.017

To summarize, the airplane drag polars are:

Low speed, clean: $C_D = 0.0237 + 0.0374 C_L^2$

Take-off, gear up $C_D = 0.0387 + 0.0398 C_L^2$

Take-off, gear down $C_D = 0.0557 + 0.0398 C_L^2$

Landing, gear up $C_D = 0.0837 + 0.0424 C_L^2$

Landing, gear down $C_D = 0.1007 + 0.0424 C_L^2$

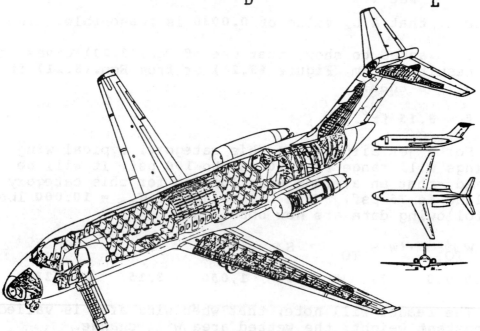

McDONNELL-DOUGLAS DC9-10

3.4.3 Summary of FAR 23 Climb Requirements

The FAR 23 climb requirements are contained in Ref.8. The climb requirements are given for two flight conditions: take-off and balked landing.

These requirements must be met with the power (or thrust) available minus installation losses and minus losses caused by accessory operation. For reciprocating engine powered airplanes, the engine power must be that for 80 percent humidity at and below standard temperature. For turbine powered airplanes, the engine thrust (or power) must be that for 34 percent humidity

and standard temperature plus 50°F. FAR 23.45 provides more details.

The take-off climb requirements of FAR 23.65 (AEO = All Engines Operating) and FAR 23.67 (OEI = One Engine Inoperative) can be summarized as follows:

3.4.3.1 FAR 23.65 (AEO)

All airplanes must have a minimum climb rate at sealevel of 300 fpm and a steady climb angle of at least 1:12 for landplanes and 1:15 for seaplanes, in the following configuration:

1) Not more than maximum continuous power on all engines
2) Landing gear retracted
3) Flaps in the take-off position
4) Cowl flaps as required for proper engine cooling (FAR 23.1041-1047).

For turbine powered airplanes, there is an additional requirement for a steady climb gradient of at least 4 percent at a pressure altitude of 5,000 ft and at 81°F, under the same configuration conditions 1-4.

3.4.3.2 FAR 23.67 (OEI)

For multiengine (reciprocating engines) airplanes with $W_{TO} > 6,000$ lbs, the steady climb rate must be at least $0.027V_{s_0}^2$ fpm, at 5,000 ft altitude, where V_{s_0} is in kts.

This requirement applies with the airplane in the

following configuration:

1) Critical engine inoperative and its propeller in the minimum drag position
2) Remaining engines at no more than maximum continuous power
3) Landing gear retracted
4) Wing flaps in the most favorable position
5) Cowl flaps as required for proper engine cooling (FAR 23.1041-1047)

For multiengine (reciprocating engines) airplanes with W_{TO} < 6,000 lbs, and with V_{s_0} > 61 kts the previous requirements also apply.

For multiengine (reciprocating engines) airplanes with W_{TO} < 6,000 lbs, and with V_{s_0} < 61 kts the requirement is that the steady climb rate at 5,000 ft altitude must be determined. Note, that this implies that a negative climb rate with one engine inoperative is allowed.

For turbine powered airplanes, the following requirements apply regardless of the weight:

a) minimum climb gradient of 1.2 percent or minimum climb rate of $0.027V_{s_0}^2$ at 5,000 ft, standard atmosphere, whichever is the most critical.

b) minimum climb gradient of 0.6 percent or minimum climb rate of $0.014V_{s_0}^2$ at 5,000 ft pressure altitude and $81^{\circ}F$, whichever is the most critical.

These requirements apply in the configurations previously given.

The balked landing climb requirements of FAR 23.77 can be summarized as follows:

3.4.3.3 FAR 23.77 (AEO)

The steady climb angle shall be at least 1:30 with the airplane in the following configuration:

a) Take-off power on all engines

b) Landing gear down

c) Flaps in landing position, unless they can be safely retracted in two seconds without loss of altitude and without requiring exceptional pilot skills

For turbine powered airplanes it is also necessary to show, that a zero steady climb rate can be maintained at a pressure altitude of 5,000 ft and 81°F in the aforementioned configuration.

The reader should note that <u>positive</u> engine-out climb performance, for FAR 23 certified airplanes in the landing configuration, <u>is not required!</u>

3.4.4 Sizing Method for FAR 23 Climb Requirements

Reference 11 contains rapid methods for estimating rate-of-climb (RC) and climb gradient (CGR) of an airplane.

3.4.4.1 Sizing to FAR 23 rate-of-climb requirements

Equations 6.15 and 6.16 of Reference 11 contain all ingredients needed for sizing to rate-of-climb criteria:

$$RC = \text{Rate of climb} = dh/dt = 33,000 \times RCP \qquad (3.23)$$

where:

RCP = Rate of climb Parameter =

$$\{\eta_p/(W/P)\} - [\{(W/S)^{1/2}\}/\{19(C_L^{3/2}/C_D)\sigma^{1/2}\}] \qquad (3.24)$$

The reader should note that RC in Eqn.(3.23) is given in fpm.

To maximize RC, it is evidently necessary to make $C_L^{3/2}/C_D$ as large as possible. This is achieved when:

$$C_{L_{RC_{max}}} = (3C_{D_0}\pi Ae)^{1/2} \qquad (3.25)$$

and:

$$C_{D_{RC_{max}}} = 4C_{D_0} \qquad (3.26)$$

which yields:

$$(C_L^{3/2}/C_D)_{max} = 1.345(Ae)^{3/4}/C_{D_0}^{1/4} \qquad (3.27)$$

Figure 3.23 shows how A and C_{D_0} affect the value of $(C_L^{3/2}/C_D)_{max}$ for an example case. Observe that Figure 3.23 also shows the corresponding lift coefficient, $C_{L_{RC_{max}}}$.

3.4.4.2 Sizing to FAR 23 climb gradient requirements

Equations (6.29) and (6.30) of Reference 11 contain all ingredients needed for sizing to climb gradient criteria:

$$CGR = \text{Climb gradient} = (dh/dt)/V \qquad (3.28)$$

and:

$$CGRP = \text{Climb gradient parameter} =$$
$$\{CGR + (L/D)^{-1}\}/C_L^{1/2}, \qquad (3.29)$$

where:

$$CGRP = 18.97\eta_p\sigma^{1/2}/(W/P)(W/S)^{1/2} \qquad (3.30)$$

To find the best possible climb gradient, it is necessary to find the minimum value of CGRP. This minimum value depends on the lift coefficient and on the corresponding lift-to-drag ratio. A problem is, that the minimum value of CGRP is usually found at a value of C_L very close to $C_{L_{max}}$.

Some margin relative to stall speed is always desired. FAR 23 does not specify this margin. Instead, FAR 23 demands, that the manufacturer clearly identify to the operator, what the speed for best rate of climb is. There is no requirement to identify the speed for best climb gradient. It is suggested to the reader, to ensure that a margin of 0.2 exists between $C_{L_{max}}$ and $C_{L_{climb}}$.

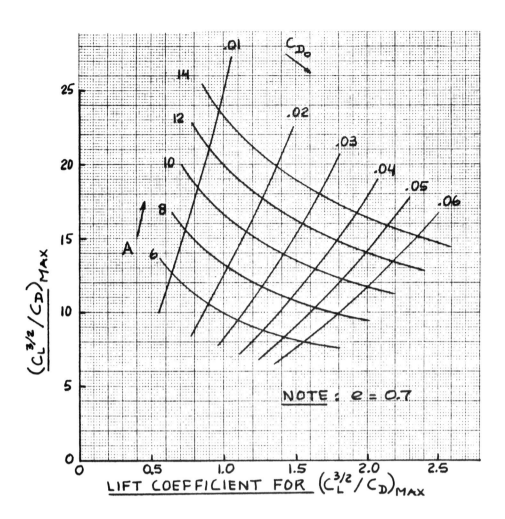

Figure 3.23 Effect of Aspect Ratio and Zero-lift Drag on $(C_L^{3/2}/C_D)_{max}$ and the Lift Coefficient Where This Occurs

SAAB-FAIRCHILD 340

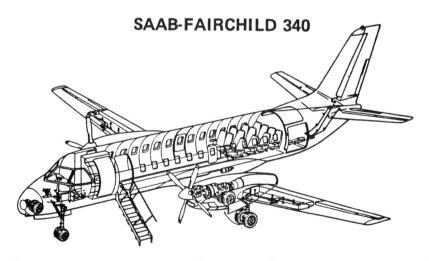

3.4.5 Example of FAR 23 Climb Sizing

It is required to size a twin engine propeller driven airplane with a take-off weight of 7,000 lbs and a landing weight of 7,000 lbs, to the FAR 23 climb requirements.

Referring to sub-section 3.4.3 it is seen that this airplane must meet the following requirements:

FAR 23.65 (AEO): RC $\geqslant$ 300 fpm
CGR $\geqslant$ 1/12 rad
Configuration: gear up, take-off flaps, max. cont. power on all engines.

FAR 23.67 (OEI): RC $\geqslant$ $0.027V_{s_0}^2$ fpm at 5,000 ft

Configuration: gear up, flaps most favorable, stopped propeller feathered, take-off power on operating engine.

FAR 23.77 (AEO): CGR $\geqslant$ 1/30 rad
Configuration: gear down, landing flaps, take-off power on all engines.

The climb sizing calculations proceed as follows:

3.4.5.1 Sizing to rate-of-climb requirements

From Eqn.(3.23):

$$RCP = (33,000)^{-1}dh/dt = (33,000)^{-1}RC$$

For FAR 23.65: $RCP = (33,000)^{-1} \times 300 = 0.0091$ hp/lbs.

For FAR 23.67: V_{s_0} needs to be computed first.

Assuming that flaps-up represents the most favorable case (this has to be checked later!) and that $C_{L_{max}} = 1.7$ (consistent with Table 3.1, flaps-up), the value of V_{s_0} at 5,000 ft is found from:

$$W = C_{L_{max}} (1/2)\rho V_{s_0}^2 S,$$

or:

$$V_{s_0} = \{(2W/S)/\rho C_{L_{max}}\}^{1/2}$$

For W/S a range of 20-50 psf will be investigated. The density of the atmosphere at 5,000 ft is

0.002049 slugs/ft^3. The following table can now be constructed:

$(W/S)_{TO}$	V_{s_0}		RC	RCP
psf	fps	kts	fpm	hp/lbs
20	107	63	107	0.0032
30	131	78	164	0.0050
40	152	90	219	0.0066
50	169	100	270	0.0082

Next, the drag polars of this airplane need to be estimated. This will be done using the method discussed in Sub-section 3.4.1.

From Figure 3.22 the wetted area of this airplane is seen to be in the neighbourhood of 1,060 ft^2. From Figure 3.21 this yields f = 5 ft^2 if c_f is taken to be 0.0050.

The effect of wing loading on the zero lift drag will be neglected. An average wing loading of 35 psf will be assumed. This yields: C_{D_0} = 5/200 = 0.0250.

For 'e', a value of 0.80 will be assumed. For aspect ratio, A a value of 8 will be used.

The following additional assumptions will also be made:

For take-off flaps: ΔC_{D_0} = 0.0150

For landing flaps: ΔC_{D_0} = 0.0600

For landing gear: ΔC_{D_0} = 0.0200

The drag polar for the FAR 23.65 requirement is now:

$$C_D = 0.0250 + 0.0150 + C_L^2/20.1$$

$$C_D = 0.0400 + C_L^2/20.1$$

With this drag polar the value of $\{C_L^{3/2}/C_D\}_{max}$ = 12.1.

From Eqn.(3.24) it now follows that:

$$[0.8/(W/P) - \{(W/S)^{1/2}/19 \times 12.1 \times 1.0\}] = 0.0091,$$

where it was assumed that η_p = 0.8.

This relationship translates into the following tabular results:

$(W/S)_{TO}$	W/P cont.	W/P take-off
psf	lbs/hp	lbs/hp
20	28.1	25.5
30	24.3	22.1
40	21.9	19.9
50	20.1	18.3
	:1.1	

On the bais of typical piston engine data, the ratio $P_{to}/P_{max.cont.}$ was taken to be 1.1

Figure 3.24 shows the range of W/S and W/P values for which the FAR 23.65 climb requirement is satisfied.

For the FAR 23.67 requirement the drag polar is:

$$C_D = 0.0250 + 0.0050 + C_L^2/20.1$$
$$\text{stopped propeller}$$

$$= 0.0300 + C_L^2/20.1$$

In this case, the value of $\{C_L^{3/2}/C_D\}_{max}$ is: 13.0.

Using Eqn.(3.24) again, but now at 5,000 ft:

$$[0.8/(W/P) - (W/S)^{1/2}/19 \times 13 \times 0.8617^{1/2}] = RCP, \text{ or:}$$

$$[0.8/(W/P) - (W/S)^{1/2}/229] = RCP,$$

where RCP is the previously determined function of wing loading, since in FAR 23.67 the climb performance is a function of V_{s_o}.

The following tabular relationship can now be constructed:

$(W/S)_{TO}$	W/P take-off one engine 5,000 ft	W/P take-off two engines 5,000 ft	W/P take-off two engines sealevel
psf	lbs/hp	lbs/hp	lbs/hp
20	35.2	17.6	15.0
30	27.7	13.9	11.8
40	23.4	11.7	9.9
50	20.5	10.3	8.8
	:2	x0.85	

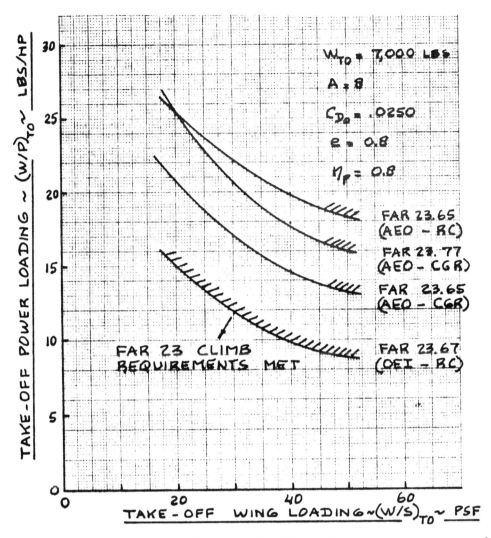

Figure 3.24 Effect of FAR 23 Climb Requirements on the
Allowable Values of Take-off Thrust-to-Weight
Ratio and Take-off Wing Loading

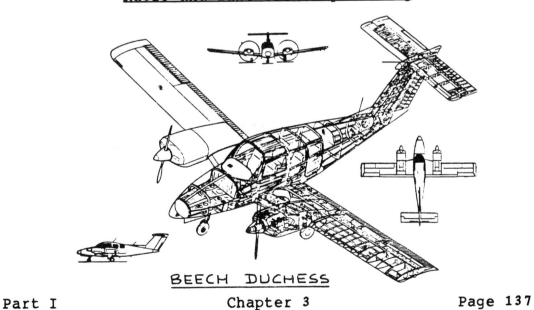

BEECH DUCHESS

The take-off power ratio between 5,000 ft and sealevel was assumed to be 0.85. This ratio is fairly typical for normally aspirated piston engines.

Figure 3.24 also shows how this requirement compares to that of FAR 23.65.

3.4.5.2 Sizing to climb gradient requirements

Climb gradient requirements are computed with the help of Eqn.(3.29):

$$CGRP = 18.97\eta_p\sigma^{1/2}/(W/P)(W/S)^{1/2} = \{CGR + (L/D)^{-1}\}/C_L^{1/2}$$

For the FAR 23.65 requirement: CGR = 1/12 = 0.0833. The drag polar for this case was already found to be:

$$C_D = 0.0400 + C_L^2/20.1$$

It will be assumed now, that with take-off flaps the value of $C_{L_{max}}$ = 1.8. Observing a margin of $\Delta C_L = 0.2$:

$$C_{L_{climb}} = 1.6$$

This yields $(L/D)_{climb} = 9.6$

Therefore:

$$CGRP = (0.0833 + 1/9.6)/1.6^{1/2} = 0.1482$$

This requirement now yields:

$$(W/P)(W/S)^{1/2} = 18.97 \times 0.8/0.1482 = 102.4$$

The following tabular relationship can now be constructed:

$(W/S)_{TO}$ psf	W/P max. cont. lbs/hp	W/P max. take-off lbs/hp
20	22.9	20.8
30	18.7	17.0
40	16.2	14.7
50	14.5	13.2
	x0.85	

Figure 3.24 also shows how this requirement compares with the previous two.

In the case of the FAR 23.77 requirement:

CGR = 1/30 = 0.0333

It will be assumed, that with the gear down and landing flaps, a value of $C_{L_{max_L}}$ = 2.0 can be achieved.

The drag polar in this case is:

C_D = 0.1050 + C_L^2/20.1

Assuming that the climb is carried out with the same margin as before:

$C_{L_{climb}}$ = 2.0 -0.2 = 1.8

The corresponding value of L/D is found to be 6.8.

This in turn means:

CGRP = (0.0333 + 1/6.8)/1.8^{12} = 0.1345

Therefore:

(W/P)(W/S)$^{1/2}$ = 18.97 x0.8/0.1345 = 113

This results in the following tabular relationship:

(W/S)$_{TO}$ psf	W/P take-off lbs/hp
20	25.3
30	20.6
40	17.9
50	16.0

Figure 3.24 compares this requirement with the other three. It is clear that the FAR 23.67 (OEI) requirement is the most critical one in this case.

The reader is asked to study the effect of aspect ratio, $C_{L_{max}}$ and C_{D_0} on these results.

3.4.6 Summary of FAR 25 Climb Requirements

The FAR 25 climb requirements are contained in Ref. 8. The climb requirements are given for two flight conditions: take-off and balked landing.

These requirements must be met with the thrust (or power) available minus installation losses and minus losses caused by accessory operation. For turbine powered airplanes, the engine thrust or power must be that for 34 percent humidity and standard temperature plus 50° F. For reciprocating engine powered airplanes, the engine power must be that for 80 percent humidity at and below standard temperature. FAR 25.101 provides more details.

The take-off climb requirements of FAR 25.111 (OEI) and FAR 25.121 (OEI) can be summarized as follows:

3.4.6.1 FAR 25.111 (OEI)

The climb gradient with the critical engine inoperative must be at least:

    a) 1.2 percent for two-engine airplanes
    b) 1.5 percent for three-engine airplanes
    c) 1.7 percent for four-engine airplanes,

in the following configuration:

    1) Take-off flaps
    2) Landing gear retracted
    3) Speed is $V_2 (= 1.2V_{s_{TO}})$
    4) Remaining engines at take-off thrust or power
    5) Between 35 ft and 400 ft altitude, ground effect must be accounted for
    6) Ambient atmospheric conditions
    7) At maximum take-off weight

This is referred to as the initial climb segment requirement.

3.4.6.2 FAR 25.121 (OEI)

The climb gradient with the critical engine inoperative must be at least:

    a) positive for two-engine airplanes
    b) 0.3 percent for three-engine airplanes
    c) 0.5 percent for four-engine airplanes,

in the following configuration:

1) Take-off flaps
2) Landing gear down
3) Remaining engines at take-off thrust or power
4) Between V_{LOF} and V_2

5) In ground effect
6) Ambient atmospheric conditions
7) At maximum take-off weight

This requirement is also referred to as the transition segment climb requirement.

The so-called second segment climb requirement demands a climb gradient with one engine inoperative of no less than:

a) 2.4 percent for two-engine airplanes
b) 2.7 percent for three-engine airplanes
c) 3.0 percent for four-engine airplanes,

in the following configuration:

1) Take-off flaps
2) Landing gear retracted
3) Remaining engines at take-off thrust or power
4) At $V_2 (= 1.2 V_{s_{TO}})$
5) Out of ground effect
6) Ambient atmospheric conditions
7) At maximum take-off weight

The en-route climb requirement with one engine inoperative demands that the climb gradient be no less than:

a) 1.2 percent for two-engine airplanes
b) 1.5 percent for three-engine airplanes
c) 1.7 percent for four-engine airplanes,

in the following configuration:

1) Flaps retracted
2) Landing gear retracted
3) Remaining engines at maximum continuous thrust or power
4) At $1.25 V_s$

5) Ambient atmospheric conditions
6) At maximum take-off weight

The reader will have observed, that there is no AEO take-off climb requirement. The reason is that the OEI requirements are so severe, that climb with AEO is not a problem in FAR 25 airplanes.

The <u>landing climb requirements</u> of FAR 25.119 (AEO) and FAR 25.121 (OEI) can be summarized as follows:

3.4.6.3 FAR 25.119 (AEO)

The climb gradient may not be less than 3.2 percent at a thrust or power level corresponding to that obtained eight seconds after moving the throttles from minimum flight idle to the take-off position. This requirement applies in the following configuration:

1) Landing flaps
2) Landing gear down
3) At $1.3V_S$

4) Ambient atmospheric conditions
5) At maximum design landing weight

3.4.6.4 FAR 25.121 (OEI)

The climb gradient with the critical engine inoperative may not be less than:

a) 2.1 percent for two-engine airplanes
b) 2.4 percent for three-engine airplanes
c) 2.7 percent for four-engine airplanes,

in the following configuration:

1) Approach flaps
2) Landing gear as defined by normal AEO operating procedures
3) At no more than $1.5V_{S_A}$
4) V_{S_A} must not be more than $1.1V_{S_L}$
5) Remaining engines at take-off thrust or power
6) Ambient atmospheric conditions
7) At maximum design landing weight

These last two requirements are known as the <u>go-around or balked landing requirements.</u>

3.4.7 Sizing Method For FAR 25 Climb Requirements

To size an airplane, so that it can meet the FAR 25 climb requirements it is suggested to use:

1) for propeller driven airplanes: Eqns.(3.23) and (3.28) of Sub-section 3.4.3

2) for jet powered airplanes:

   with one engine inoperative (OEI):

   $$(T/W) = \{N/(N - 1)\}\{(L/D)^{-1} + CGR\} \qquad (3.31a)$$

   with all engines operating (AEO):

   $$(T/W) = \{(L/D)^{-1} + CGR\} \qquad (3.31b)$$

   where:

   CGR is the required climb gradient (this is the same as the flight path angle γ),

   N is the number of engines,

   L/D is the lift-to-drag ratio in the flight condition being analyzed, and

   T/W is the thrust-to-weight ratio in the flight condition being analyzed.

The reader note carefully, that (T/W) and (L/D) are those for take-off or for landing, depending on the requirement being analyzed.

The process of sizing for climb requirements amounts to finding relations between $(W/S)_{TO}$, $(T/W)_{TO}$ or $(W/P)_{TO}$ and A for a given value of W_{TO}.

3.4.8 Example of FAR 25 Climb Sizing

It is required to size a twin engine jet transport with: W_{TO} = 125,000 lbs and W_L = 115,000 lbs to FAR 25 climb requirements.

From the climb requirements in Sub-section 3.4.6 it follows that this airplane must be sized to the following requirements:

For Take-off climb:

FAR 25.111 (OEI): CGR > 0.012
Configuration: gear up, take-off flaps, take-off thrust on remaining engines, ground effect, $1.2V_{s_{TO}}$.

FAR 25.121 (OEI): CGR > 0
Configuration: gear down, take-off flaps, take-off thrust on remaining engines, ground effect, speed between V_{LOF} and $1.2V_{s_{TO}}$.

FAR 25.121 (OEI): CGR > 0.024
Configuration: gear up, take-off flaps, no ground effect, take-off thrust on remaining engines, $1.2V_{s_{TO}}$.

FAR 25.121 (OEI): CGR > 0.012
Configuration: gear up, flaps up, en route climb altitude, maximum continuous thrust on remaining engines, $1.25V_s$.

For Landing Climb:

FAR 25.119 (AEO): CGR > 0.032
Configuration: gear down, landing flaps, take-off thrust on all engines, maximum design landing weight, $1.3V_{s_L}$.

FAR 25.121 (OEI): CGR > 0.021
Configuration: gear down, approach flaps, take-off thrust on remaining engines, $1.5V_{s_A}$.

All FAR 25 climb criteria involve the climb gradient, CGR and the lift-to-drag ratio of the airplane in some configuration, as seen from Eqn.(3.31a and b). It is therefore necessary to obtain an initial estimate of the drag polar of this airplane. The method of Sub-section 3.4.1 will be used to find this drag polar.

From Figure 3.22b the wetted area of this airplane is about 8,000 ft^2 for the 125,000 lbs take-off weight. From Figure 3.21 this yields f = 23 ft^2 if c_f is taken to be 0.0030. Assuming an average wing loading of 100 psf it is found that S = 1,250 ft^2. From this it follows: C_{D_0} = 0.0184.

The following drag polar data will now be assumed:

Configuration	C_{D_0}	A	e	C_{D_i}	$C_{L_{max}}$
Clean	0.0184	10	0.85	$C_L^2/26.7$	1.4
Take-off flaps	0.0334	10	0.80	$C_L^2/25.1$	2.0
Landing flaps	0.0784	10	0.75	$C_L^2/23.6$	2.8
Gear down	0.0150 for incremental zero-lift drag coefficient				no effect

The climb sizing calculations can now proceed as follows:

FAR 25.111 (OEI):

$(T/W)_{TO}$ = 2{ 1/(L/D) + 0.012}, at $1.2V_{s_{TO}}$.

Since the value assumed for $C_{L_{TO_{max}}}$ = 2.0, the actual lift coefficient in this flight condition is 2.0/1.44 = 1.4.

The drag polar is: C_D = 0.0334 + $C_L^2/25.1$.

This yields L/D = 12.6. Therefore:

$(T/W)_{TO}$ = 2{1/12.6 + 0.012} = 0.182.

However, this does not account for the 50°F temperature effect. Typical turbofan data indicate that at sealevel, the ratio of maximum thrust at standard temperature to that at a 50°F higher temperature is 0.80. Thus, for sizing purposes: $(T/W)_{TO} = 0.182/0.8 = 0.23$.

<u>FAR 25.121 (OEI)</u> (gear down, t.o. flaps):

$(T/W)_{TO} = 2\{ 1/(L/D) + 0\}$, between V_{LOF} and V_2.

It will be assumed, that $V_{LOF} = 1.1 V_{s_{TO}}$.

Because $C_{L_{TO_{max}}} = 2.0$, $C_{L_{LOF}} = 2.0/1.1^2 = 1.65$.

The drag polar is: $C_D = 0.0484 + C_L^2/25.1$.

This yields $L/D = 10.5$. Therefore:

$(T/W)_{TO} = 2\{1/10.5\} = 0.19$.

At V_2, the value of the lift coefficient is:

$2.0/1.44 = 1.4$.

Therefore $L/D = 11.1$ and $(T/W)_{TO} = 2\{1/11.1\} = 0.18$.

It is seen that the requirement at V_{LOF} is the more

critical. Correcting for temperature this requirement now becomes: $(T/W)_{TO} = 0.19/0.8 = 0.24$.

<u>FAR 25.121 (OEI)</u> (gear up, t.o.flaps):

$(T/W)_{TO} = 2\{1/(L/D) + 0.024\}$ at $1.2\ V_{s_{TO}}$.

The lift coefficient is $2.0/1.44 = 1.4$.

The drag polar is: $C_D = 0.0334 + C_L^2/25.1$.

This yields $L/D = 12.6$. Therefore:

$(T/W)_{TO} = 2\{1/12.6 + 0.024\} = 0.21$.

With the temperature correction this becomes: $(T/W)_{TO} = 0.21/0.8 = 0.26$.

<u>FAR 25.121 (OEI)</u> (gear up, flaps up):

$(T/W)_{TO} = 2\{1/L/D + 0.012\}$ at $1.25 V_s$.

Since in the clean configuration $C_{L_{max}} = 1.4$,

$C_L = 1.4/1.25^2 = 0.9$.

The drag polar is: $C_D = 0.0184 + C_L^2/26.7$.

This yields: $L/D = 18.5$. Therefore:

$(T/W)_{TO} = 2\{1/18.5 + 0.012\} = 0.136$.

However, this is for maximum continuous thrust. A typical value for the ratio of maximum continuous thrust to maximum take-off thrust is 0.94 for turbofan engines. With this correction and with the temperature correction, the requirement is: $(T/W)_{TO} = 0.136/0.94/0.8 = 0.18$.

FAR 25.119 (AEO) (balked landing):

$(T/W)_L = \{1/L/D + 0.032\}$ at $1.3V_{s_L}$.

In the landing configuration it was assumed that $C_{L_{max_L}} = 2.8$, the lift coefficient in this case is:

$2.8/1.3^2 = 1.66$.

The drag polar now is: $C_D = 0.0934 + C_L^2/23.6$.

This yields: $L/D = 7.9$. Therefore:

$(T/W)_L = \{1/7.9 + 0.032\} = 0.16$.

Since the design landing weight is 115,000 lbs, this translates into the following take-off requirement, after also applying the temperature correction:

$(T/W)_{TO} = 0.16(115,000/125,000)/0.8 = 0.19$.

FAR 25.121 (OEI) (balked landing):

$(T/W)_L = 2\{1/(L/D) + 0.021\}$ at $1.5 V_{s_A}$.

It will be assumed, that in the approach configuration, $C_{L_{max_A}} = 2.4$. This results in the following value for approach lift coefficient:

$C_{L_A} = 2.4/1.5^2 = 1.07$

With approach flaps, the drag increment due to flaps will be assumed to be halfway between landing and take-off flaps. This yields for the drag polar:

$$C_D = 0.0709 + C_L^2/23.6.$$

Therefore: $L/D = 9.0$ and:

$$(T/W)_L = 2\{1/9.0 + 0.021\} = 0.26.$$

With the weight and temperature corrections as before, it follows that:

$$(T/W)_{TO} = 0.26(115,000/125,000)/0.8 = 0.30.$$

It appears that this last requirement is the most critical one for this airplane. Figure 3.25 shows how the six climb requirements compare with each other.

The reader is asked to investigate the effect of aspect ratio, $C_{L_{max}}$ and C_{D_0} on these results.

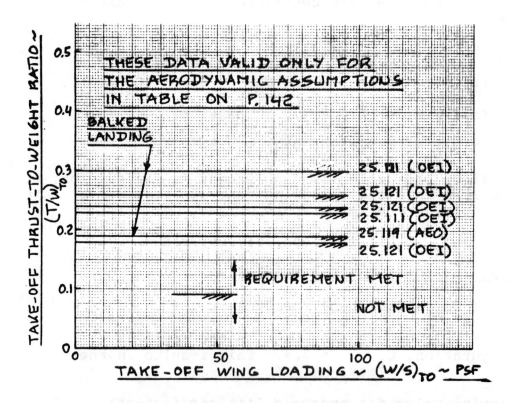

Figure 3.25 Effect of FAR 25 Climb Requirements on the Allowable Values of Take-off Thrust-to-Weight Ratio and Take-off Wing Loading

3.4.9 Summary of Military Climb Requirements

Military requirements for climb characteristics are usually specific to an RFP. Those requirements that deal with climb rate or climb gradient minima are given in Ref.15: MIL-C-005011B and in Appendix B of Part VII.

The requirements apply to <u>single engine airplanes and to multi engine airplanes with the most critical engine inoperative.</u>

The requirements must be met at W_{TO} and with applicable external stores.

A summary of these requirements now follows:

1) Take-off climb requirements

a) Ref. 15, par.3.4.2.4.1:

At take-off speed, $V_{TO} = 1.1V_{s_{TO}}$, the climb gradient must be at least 0.005.
Configuration: gear down, flaps take-off, maximum power.

b) Ref. 15, par.3.4.2.5:

At the 50 ft obstacle and at $1.15V_{s_{TO}}$, the climb gradient must be at least 0.025.
Configuration: gear up, flaps take-off, maximum power.

2) Landing climb requirements

a) Ref. 15, par.3.4.2.11:

At the 50 ft obstacle and at $1.2V_{s_{PA}}$ the climb gradient must be at least 0.025.
Configuration: gear up, flaps approach, maximum <u>dry</u> power.

<u>NOTE WELL:</u> these climb requirements can be analyzed with the Sizing Methods of Sub-sections 3.4.4 and 3.4.7!!

Frequently, military airplanes have to meet certain time-to-climb and ceiling requirements. A method for rapid sizing to these requirements is presented in Sub-section 3.4.10.

Particularly for fighter airplanes, where combat maneuverability plays an important role, there frequently exist requirements for a certain amount of specific excess power, P_s. Sub-section 3.4.11 presents a method for sizing to specific excess power requirements.

3.4.10 Sizing for Time-to-climb and Ceiling Requirements

3.4.10.1 Sizing to time-to-climb requirements

Figure 3.26 shows an assumed linear relationship between rate-of-climb and altitude. Whether or not this relation in reality is linear depends on the engine and on the airplane characteristics as well as on the flight speed at which the climb is carried out.

Figure 3.26 introduces the following quantities:

RC_0 = rate of climb at sealevel in fpm

RC_h = rate of climb at altitude, h in fpm

The reader is asked to show, that the rate-of-climb at a given altitude can be written as:

$$RC_h = RC_0(1 - h/h_{abs}) \tag{3.32}$$

Typical values for h_{abs} are given in Table 3.7 for different propulsive installations.

When sizing an airplane to a given time-to-climb requirement, the time-to-climb, t_{cl} will be specified.

A value for h_{abs} can be selected from Table 3.7 unless it is specified in the mission specification. The rate-of-climb at sealevel, RC_0 can be calculated from:

$$RC_0 = (h_{abs}/t_{cl})\ln(1 - h/h_{abs})^{-1} \tag{3.33}$$

Having determined RC_0, it is possible to find the required power loading or thrust-to-weight ratio as follows:

For shallow flight path angles: $\gamma < 15$ deg.

a) For propeller driven airplanes:
   from Eqns.(3.23) and (3.24)

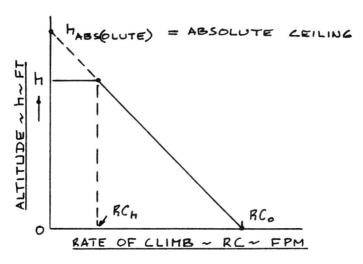

Figure 3.26 Linearized Rate-of-climb With Altitude

Table 3.7 Typical Values for the Absolute Ceiling, h_{abs}
===

Airplane Type	h_{abs} (ft)x10^{-3}
Airplanes with piston-propeller combinations:	
normally aspirated	12-18
supercharged	15-25
Airplanes with turbojet or turbofan engines:	
Commercial	40-50
Military	40-55
Fighters	55-75
Military Trainers	35-45
Airplanes with turbopropeller or propfan engines:	
Commercial	30-45
Military	30-50
Supersonic Cruise Airplanes (jets)	55-80

b) For jet driven airplanes:
   from Eqn.(3.34):

$$RC = V\{(T/W) - 1/(L/D)\} \qquad (3.34)$$

If the climb rate is to be maximized, Ref.14 shows that L/D needs to be maximized.   In that case:

$$V = [2(W/S)/\{\rho(C_{D_o}\pi Ae)^{1/2}\}]^{1/2} \qquad (3.35)$$

and:

$$(L/D)_{max} = 0.5(\pi Ae/C_{D_o})^{1/2} \qquad (3.36)$$

From Eqns.(3.23) and (3.24) or from Eqns.(3.34) through (3.36) it is possible to find regions of $(T/W)_{TO}$ and $(W/S)_{TO}$ for which the climb requirements are satisfied.

For steep flight path angles: $\gamma > 15$ deg.

The reader should note that this case applies to fighter type airplanes only.

$$RC = V\sin\gamma, \qquad (3.37)$$

where:

$$\sin\gamma = \frac{T}{W}\left[P_{d1} - \sqrt{P_{d1}{}^2 - P_{d1} + \left(1 + \left(\frac{L}{D}\right)^2\right)^{-1}\left(\frac{T}{W}\right)^{-2}}\right]$$
$$(3.38)$$

and where:

$$P_{d1} = (L/D)^2/\{1 + (L/D)^2\} \qquad (3.39)$$

For best climb performance, the value of L/D in Eqn.(3.39) can be taken to be $(L/D)_{max}$.

3.4.10.2 Sizing to ceiling requirements

When sizing to a given ceiling requirement, the minimum required rate of climb at the ceiling altitude is specified.   Table 3.8 defines the minimum climb rates for different ceilings.

The rate of climb at any altitude is given by:

Table 3.8 Definition of Airplane Ceilings
===

Ceiling Type	Minimum Required Climb Rate
Absolute ceiling	0 fpm
Service ceiling	
Commercial/Piston-propeller	100 fpm
Commercial/jet	500 fpm
Military at maximum power	100 fpm
Combat ceiling	
Military/Subsonic/maximum power	500 fpm at M<1
Military/Supersonic/maximum power	1,000 fpm at M>1
Cruise ceiling	
Military/Subsonic/max.cont. power	300 fpm at M<1
Military/Supersonic/max.cont. power	1,000 fpm at M>1

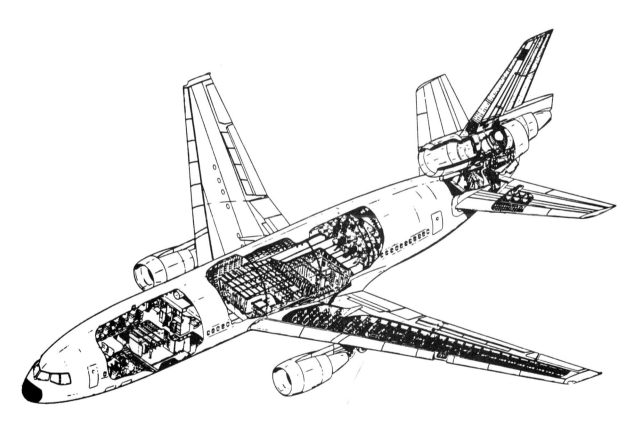

McDonnell Douglas

DC-10

a) For propeller driven airplanes:
   from Eqns.(3.23) and (3.24)

b) For jet driven airplanes:
   from Eqns.(3.34) through (3.36)

From these equations it is again possible to derive ranges of values for $(T/W)_{TO}$ and $(W/S)_{TO}$ for which the ceiling requirement is met.

3.4.11 Sizing to Specific Excess Power Requirements

Specific excess power is defined as follows:

$$P_S = dh_e/dt = (T - D)V/W, \qquad (3.40)$$

where:

$$h_e = \text{specific energy} = V^2/2g + h \qquad (3.41)$$

For certain fighter airplanes the value of P_S can be specified at a given combination of Mach number, M, weight, W and altitude, h. The reason for this is to assure combat superiority over some known or perceived threat.

To obtain the best possible P_S, Eqn.(3.40) suggests to:

a) install a high value of T/W and,
b) design for a high value of L/D.

For preliminary sizing purposes it is suggested that a range of realistic values are assumed for L/D. From Eqn.(3.40) it is then possible to determine the required value of T/W for a given value of P_S. The thus obtained value for T/W needs to be transferred to a corresponding value for $(T/W)_{TO}$ using engine data.

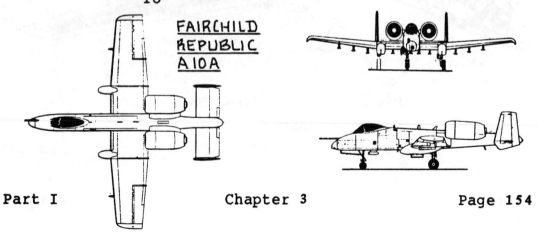

FAIRCHILD
REPUBLIC
A 10A

3.4.12 Example of Sizing to Military Climb Requirements

An attack fighter with the mission specification of Table 2.19 needs to be sized such that its climb performance meets that specified in Table 2.19.

The specification consists of two requirements:

1) RC > 500 fpm with one engine out, sealevel 95°F and at maximum take-off weight. This includes external stores.
The mission specification does not specify the airplane configuration. It is assumed, that this is gear up and flaps take-off.

2) T_{cl} = 8 min. to 40,000 ft at maximum (clean) take-off weight.

In addition, it is assumed, that the following P_s requirement must also be met:

3) P_s = 80 fps at 40,000 ft and M = 0.8, in the clean configuration and at maximum (clean) take-off weight.

First, the drag polar must be estimated. To do this, the procedure of Sub-section 3.4.1 will be used.

From p.67, it follows that W_{TO} = 64,500 lbs. This weight includes external stores! The effect of external stores is not included in the wetted area correlation of Figure 3.22b. The clean maximum take-off weight for this fighter is 64,500 - 10,000 = 54,500 lbs.

From Figure 3.22c it is found that the corresponding S_{wet} = 3,500 ft^2. This value is taken to Figure 3.21b and, assuming C_f = 0.0030, it follows that f = 10.5 ft^2.

A reasonable average wing loading for this type of attack fighter is 50 psf. This yields S_w = 1,090 ft^2. Therefore:

C_{D_0} = 10.5/1,090 = 0.0096

It will be assumed that the external stores cause an

increase in equivalent flat plate area of: $\Delta f = 3.2$ ft^2.
This yields:

$$\Delta C_{D_o} = 3.2/1,090 = 0.0030$$

The following additional assumptions are made:

Wing aspect ratio, A = 4
Oswald's efficiency factor, e = 0.8 clean and
$\qquad\qquad\qquad\qquad\qquad$ e = 0.7 flaps take-off
Incremental value for flaps take-off zero lift drag
coefficient:

$$\Delta C_{D_o} = 0.0200.$$

Compressibility drag increment, clean, at M = 0.8:

$$\Delta C_{D_o} = 0.0020.$$

The drag polars may be summarized as follows:

Clean, low speed: $\quad C_D = 0.0096 + 0.0995 C_L^2$

Clean, M = 0.8: $\qquad C_D = 0.0116 + 0.0995 C_L^2$

Take-off, gear up: $C_D = 0.0296 + 0.1137 C_L^2$

The three climb requirements will now be analyzed one by one.

Climb requirement 1): Engine out, t.o., gear up

With the help of Eqns. (3.34) through (3.36) it is now possible to determine the relation between W/S and T/W so that this climb rate is satisfied.
It will be assumed that the climb can be performed at $(L/D)_{max}$. From Eqn. (3.36) it is found that:

$$(L/D)_{max} = 8.6$$

From Eqn. (3.35) it is seen that the corresponding speed depends on wing loading and on density. The latter is to be taken on a 95°F day. In that case the corresponding temperature ratio is: 554.7/518.7 = 1.069.
The density ratio at sealevel now is:

$$\sigma = 1/1.069 = 0.935, \text{ so that } \rho = 0.002224 \text{ slugs/ft}^3.$$

With the help of Eqns. (3.34) and (3.35) it is now

possible to construct the following tabulation:

$(W/S)_{TO}$	V	RC/V	1/L/D	$(T/W)_{TO}$	$(T/W)_{TO}$	$(T/W)_{TO}$
psf	fps			one eng.	two eng.	two eng.
				$95^{\circ}F$	$95^{\circ}F$	sls
	(3.35)			(3.34)		
40	265	0.031	0.116	0.147	0.294	0.346
60	325	0.026	0.116	0.142	0.284	0.334
80	375	0.022	0.116	0.138	0.276	0.325
100	420	0.020	0.116	0.136	0.272	0.320
				x2		:0.85

To obtain the numbers in the last column, it was

assumed that for the $95^{\circ}F$ day, the thrust is 0.85 times
that at sealevel standard (sls).

Figure 3.27 shows the region of $(W/S)_{TO}$ and $(T/W)_{TO}$

for which this climb requirement is met.

Climb Requirement 2: Clean, without stores

The time-to-climb to 40,000 ft is to be 8 min. in
the clean configuration. It will be assumed that the
absolute ceiling is 45,000 ft. From Eqn.(3.33) it
follows that:

$$RC_0 = (45,000/8)\ln(1 - 40/45) = 12,359 \text{ fpm} = 206 \text{ fps}$$

Because this is a fighter airplane, the climb angle
is probably steep. Therefore, the method of Eqns.(3.37)
through (3.39) will be used in the sizing process.

It is assumed, that the climb will take place at
$(L/D)_{max}$.

Since $C_{D_0} = 0.0096$, it follows from Eqn.(3.36) that:

$(L/D)_{max} = 16.2$. The corresponding speed follows again

from Eqn.(3.35).

The value for P_{dl} may be found from Eqn.(3.39) as:

0.996. With Eqns.(3.37) and (3.38) it also follows that:

$$RC_0 = 0.996V(T/W)$$

It is now possible to construct the following
tabulation:

$(W/S)_{TO}$	$(W/S)_{TO}$	V	$(T/W)_{TO}$	$(T/W)_{TO}$
clean (without stores)	maximum (with stores)	(3.35)	clean (without stores)	maximum (with stores)
psf	psf	fps		
40	47	329	0.629	0.531
60	71	403	0.514	0.434
80	95	465	0.445	0.376
100	118	520	0.398	0.336
	:1.18			:1.18

The factor 1.18 represents the ratio of take-off weight with stores (64,500 lbs) to that without stores (54,500 lbs).

Figure 3.27 shows regions of $(W/S)_{TO}$ and $(T/W)_{TO}$ where this requirement is met.

<u>Climb Requirement 3: Clean, without stores</u>

With P_s = 80 fps, Eqn.(3.40) can be rearranged to yield:

$$(T/W) = 80/V + 1/(L/D)$$

At M = 0.8 and 40,000 ft, the dynamic pressure is:

$$\bar{q} = 1482 \times 0.1851 \times M^2 = 176 \text{ psf}$$

The clean drag polar at M = 0.8 was previously given. The clean maximum weight is 54,500 lbs. The following tabulation can now be constructed:

$(W/S)_{TO}$	$\bar{q}$	C_L	C_D	L/D	1/(L/D)	V
clean (without stores)						
psf	psf					fps
40	176	0.23	0.0169	13.6	0.074	774
60	176	0.34	0.0231	14.7	0.068	774
80	176	0.45	0.0317	14.2	0.070	774
100	176	0.57	0.0439	13.0	0.077	774

(W/S)$_{TO}$	80/V	(T/W) at 40K M = 0.8	(T/W)$_{TO}$ sls
maximum (with stores) psf			
47	0.103	0.177	0.96
71	0.103	0.171	0.92
95	0.103	0.173	0.93
118	0.103	0.180	0.97

x5.4

The last column was obtained by multiplying (T/W) at 40,000 ft and M = 0,8 by 5.4, which is the pressure ratio for that altitude. This corresponds roughly to the thrust ratio for these two conditions.

From typical engine data it can be observed that at high altitude and subsonic flight no significant change in thrust occurs between M = 0 and M = 0.8.

Figure 3.27 shows the region of (W/S)$_{TO}$ and (T/W)$_{TO}$

where this specific excess power requirement is met. It is clear that this requirement is by far the more critical one in this case.

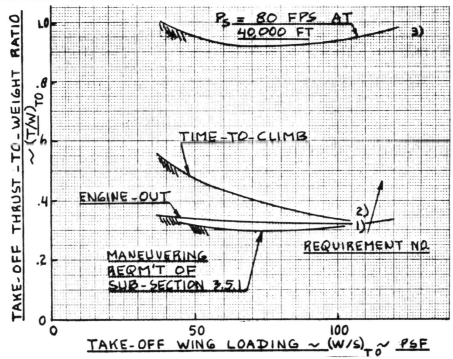

Figure 3.27 Effect of Military Climb Requirements on the Allowable Values of Take-off Thrust-to-Weight Ratio and Take-off Wing Loading

3.5 SIZING TO MANEUVERING REQUIREMENTS

Specific requirements for sustained maneuvering capability (including sometimes specific turn rate) are often contained in the mission specification for utility, agricultural, aerobatic or for military airplanes.

Sustained maneuvering requirements are usually formulated in terms of a combination of sustained load factor (g's) to be pulled at some combination of speed and altitude.

The sustained maneuvering capability of an airplane depends strongly on its maximum lift coefficient and on its installed thrust.

For equilibrium perpendicular to the flight path, it is necessary that:

$$nW = C_L \bar{q} S = 1,482 \delta M^2 C_L S \tag{3.42}$$

The maximum load factor capability of an airplane, n_{max} can be found from Eqn.(3.42) as:

$$n_{max} = (1,482 C_{L_{max}} \delta M^2)/(W/S) \tag{3.43}$$

This load factor can be sustained as long as there is sufficient thrust. Since:

$$T = C_{D_0} \bar{q} S + (C_L^2/\pi A e) \bar{q} S \tag{3.44}$$

After dividing Eqn.(3.44) by W and rearranging:

$$(T/W) =$$

$$\bar{q} C_{D_0}/(W/S) + (W/S)(n_{max})^2/(\pi A e \bar{q}) \tag{3.45}$$

If some maximum load factor, n_{max} is desired on a

sustained basis at a given combination of Mach number, M and altitude (δ), then Eqn.(3.45) can be used to find the relation between T/W and W/S, for a given value of C_{D_0}. The latter can be found with the methods discussed

in Sub-section 3.4.1.

If a requirement is included for a specific minimum turn rate, the following equation may be used:

$$\dot{\psi} = (g/V)(n^2 - 1)^{1/2} \tag{3.46}$$

This equation is derived in Ref.14, p.493.

If turn rate is specified at a given speed, the required sustained load factor, n may be found from:

$$n_{reqd} = \{(V\dot{\psi}/g)^2 + 1\}^{1/2} \qquad (3.47)$$

Equation (3.45) can then be used to find the relation between (T/W) and (W/S) for which the turn rate requirement is satisfied.

3.5.1 Example of Sizing to a Maneuvering Requirement

The fighter with the mission specification of Table 2.19 must also meet the following maneuvering requirement: a sustained steady turn corresponding to 3.5g at sealevel, 450 kts and with a clean weight of 54,500 lbs.

It is assumed, that the clean C_{D_0} of the airplane at

M =450/661.2 = 0.68 and sealevel is 0.0096. With A =4 and e = 0.8 it follows from Eqn.(3.45) that:

$$(T/W)_{reqd} = 6.6/(W/S) + 0.00178(W/S)$$

The following tabulation can now be made:

(W/S) actual psf	(W/S)$_{TO}$ max psf	First Term	Second Term	(T/W) clean	(T/W)$_{TO}$ max M = 0.68	(T/W)$_{TO}$ max static
40	47	0.165	0.071	0.236	0.200	0.320
60	71	0.110	0.107	0.217	0.184	0.294
80	95	0.083	0.142	0.225	0.191	0.305
100	118	0.066	0.178	0.244	0.207	0.331
x1.18					:1.18	x1.6

The value of (T/W)$_{TO}$ in the last column is obtained

from that at M = 0.68 by multiplying by 1.6. This number is representative of the thrust ratio between M = 0 and M = 0.68 at sealevel. Such a number comes from typical engine data.

Figure 3.27 also shows the regions of (W/S)$_{TO}$ and

(W/S)$_{TO}$ for which the maneuvering requirement is met.

3.6 SIZING TO CRUISE SPEED REQUIREMENTS

3.6.1 Cruise Speed Sizing of Propeller Driven Airplanes

The power required to fly at some speed and altitude is given by:

$$P_{reqd} = T\overline{V} = C_D qSV \qquad (3.48)$$

This can also be written as:

$$550SHP\eta_p = 0.5\rho V^3 S C_D \qquad (3.49)$$

Cruise speeds for propeller driven airplanes are usually calculated at 75 to 80 percent power. In that case it can be shown that the induced drag is small compared to the profile drag. Frequently, the assumption:

$$C_{D_i} = 0.1 C_{D_o} \qquad (3.50)$$

is made.

Loftin (ref.11) showed, that because of this fact, cruise speed turns out to be proportional to the following factor:

$$V_{cr} \propto [\{(W/S)/(W/P)\}(\eta_p/\sigma C_{D_o})^{-1}]^{1/3} \qquad (3.51)$$

From this, Loftin derived the fact that:

$$V_{cr} \propto I_p \qquad (3.52)$$

where:
$$I_p = \{(W/S)/\sigma(W/P)\}^{1/3} \qquad (3.53)$$

The parameter I_p is called the power index.

Figures 3.28, 3.29 and 3.30 show how V_{cr} is related to I_p for a range of example airplanes. These figures can therefore be used as a first estimate for I_p for a given desired cruise speed. From that in turn it is possible to determine the relationship between (W/S) and (W/P) needed to meet a given cruise speed requirement.

It is possible to use this method to reconstruct C_{D_o} from measured speed and power data.

The next Sub-section presents an application.

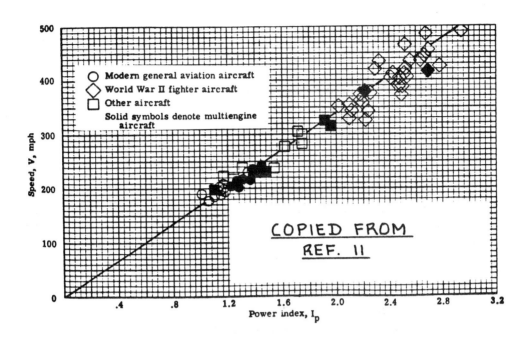

Figure 3.28 Correlation of Airplane Speed with Power
          Index for Retractable Gear, Cantilevered
          Wing Configurations

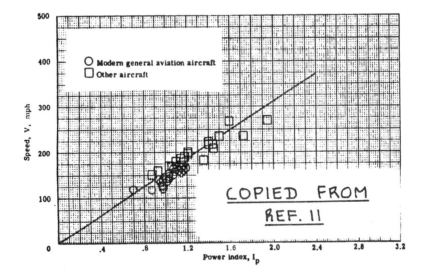

Figure 3.29 Correlation of Airplane Speed with Power
          Index for Fixed Gear, Cantilevered
          Configurations

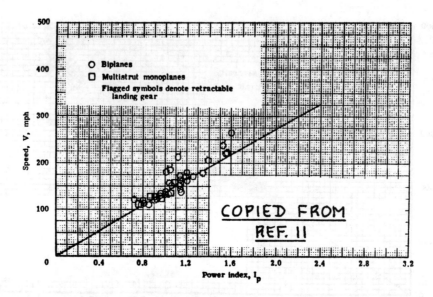

Figure 3.30 Correlation of Airplane Speed with Power
Index for Biplanes and Strutted Monoplanes
with Fixed Gear

Table 3.9 Typical Values for Zero-lift Drag Coefficient
===
and Maximum Lift-to-drag Ratio
===============================

Airplane Type	C_{D_0}	A	e	$(L/D)_{max}$
Boeing 247D	0.0212	6.55	0.75	13.5
Douglas DC-3	0.0249	9.14	0.75	14.7
Boeing B-17G	0.0236	7.58	0.75	13.8
Seversky P-35	0.0251	5.89	0.62	10.7
Piper J-3 Cub	0.0373	5.81	0.75	9.6
Beechcraft D17S	0.0348	6.84	0.76	10.8
Consolidated B-24J	0.0406	11.55	0.74	12.9
Martin B-26F	0.0314	7.66	0.75	12.0
North American P-51D	0.0161	5.86	0.69	14.0
Lockheed L.1049G	0.0211	9.17	0.75	16.0
Piper Cherokee	0.0358	6.02	0.76	10.0
Cessna Skyhawk	0.0319	7.32	0.75	11.6
Beech Bonanza V-35	0.0192	6.20	0.75	13.8
Cessna Cardinal RG	0.0223	7.66	0.63	13.0

Note: These data are copied from Ref.11, Table 5.I.

3.6.2 A Method for Finding C_{D_0} from Speed and Power Data.

Loftin, in Ref.11, Eqn.(6.3) derives the following equation:

$$V = 77.3\{\eta_p(W/S)/\sigma C_D(W/P)\}^{1/3} \qquad (3.54)$$

With Eqn.(3.53) it is possible to rewrite this as:

$$C_D = \eta_p 77.3^3 (I_p/V)^3 \qquad (3.55)$$

By now assuming that in a high speed cruise condition $\eta_p = 0.85$ and that $C_{D_0} = 0.9 C_D$, Eqn.(3.55) becomes:

$$C_{D_0} = 1.114 \times 10^5 (I_p/V)^3 \qquad (3.56)$$

It must be noted that V in Eqn.(3.56) is in mph!

If for a given airplane the maximum power and speed at some altitude are given, it is possible to use Eqn.(3.56) to estimate C_{D_0}. Table 3.9 shows some results as obtained by Loftin in Ref.11.

3.6.3 Example of Cruise Speed Sizing for a Propeller Driven Airplane

The airplane of Table 2.17 must achieve a cruise speed of 250 kts at 85 percent power at 10,000 ft and at take-off weight. Size the airplane so it can do that.

Observe, that 250 kts is equivalent to 288 mph. From Figure 3.28 it follows that: $I_p = 1.7$.

At 10,000 ft, $\sigma = 0.7386$. Therefore, with Eqn.(3.53) it is found that:

$$(W/S) = 3.63(W/P)$$

Figure 3.31 shows the range of combinations of W/S and W/P for which the cruise speed requirement is met.
Note that (W/P) is at 10,000 ft. To transfer that ratio to sealevel it is necessary to multiply by the power ratio for cruise power at 10,000 ft to that at sealevel. This ratio is typically 0.7 for reciprocating engines without supercharging.

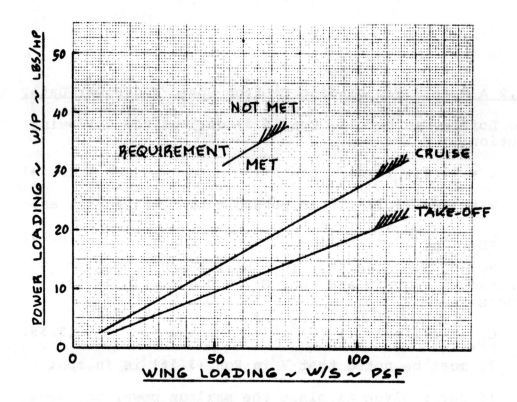

Figure 3.31 Allowable Values of Wing Loading and Thrust-
to-Weight Ratio to Meet a Given Cruise Speed

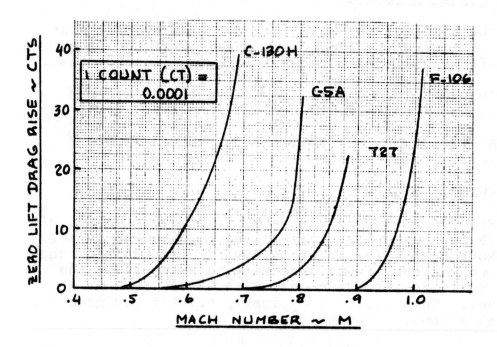

Figure 3.32 Rapid Method for Estimating Drag Rise

3.6.4 Cruise Speed Sizing of Jet Airplanes

At maximum level speed the following equations are simultaneously satisfied:

$$T_{reqd} = C_D \bar{q} S \qquad (3.57)$$

$$W = C_L \bar{q} S \qquad (3.58)$$

If a parabolic drag polar is assumed, Eqn.(3.57) can be written as:

$$T_{reqd} = C_{D_0} \bar{q} S + C_L^2 \bar{q} S / \pi A e \qquad (3.59)$$

Dividing by weight:

$$(T/W)_{reqd} = C_{D_0} \bar{q} S / W + W / \bar{q} S \pi A e \qquad (3.60)$$

If the maximum speed is specified at some combination of Mach number and altitude, then the dynamic pressure, $\bar{q}$ is known. For a given value of zero lift drag coefficient, C_{D_0}, it is possible to use Eqn.(3.60) to construct relations between T/W and W/S which satisfy the maximum speed requirements.

The maximum speed tends to be specified at a value of weight, below take-off weight, that is at:

$$W = k W_{TO}, \qquad (3.61)$$

where k is a number $0 < k < 1.0$. The required take-off wing loading must therefore be obtained from:

$$(W/S)_{TO} = k^{-1} (W/S)_{Eqn.(3.60)} \qquad (3.62)$$

Similarly, the required thrust-to-weight ratio at take-off must be reconstructed from the thrust-to-weight ratio found from Eqn.(3.60). To do this requires knowledge of how the installed thrust of the airplane varies with Mach number and with altitude.

The methodology just discussed works fine for speeds at Mach numbers below that where compressibility effects play a role. If compressibility is important (and generally above M=0.5 it is), a modification of C_{D_0} will be required. Figure (3.32) shows how ΔC_{D_0} can be quickly found.

3.6.5 Example of Sizing to Maximum Speed for a Jet

It is desired to size an airplane with W_{TO} = 10,000 lbs so that it has a maximum speed of M = 0.9 at sealevel.

At this high Mach Number, the effects of drag rise need to be accounted for.

From Figure 3.22b, at 10,000 lbs, a wetted area estimate for this airplane is: S_{wet} = 1,050 ft^2.

From Figure 3.21b, assuming a C_f = 0.0030, it is seen that: f = 3.2 ft^2.

A typical value for wing loading is taken to be 60 ft^2. This implies S = 167 ft^2 and therefore:

$$C_{D_0} = 0.0192$$

The compressibility drag increment is assumed to be 0.0030. Assuming A = 5 and e = 0.8, Eqn.(3.60) can be written as:

$$T/W = 26.6/(W/S) + (W/S)/15,080$$

The following tabulation can now be made:

$(W/S)_{TO}$	Profile Drag Term	Induced Drag Term	T/W	$(T/W)_{TO}$
			M = 0.9	static
psf				
40	0.665	0.003	0.668	1.07
60	0.443	0.004	0.447	0.72
80	0.333	0.005	0.338	0.54
100	0.266	0.007	0.273	0.44

Figure 3.33 shows the region of W/S and T/W for which the speed requirement is met. Note the advantage of high wing loading at high speed and at sealevel.

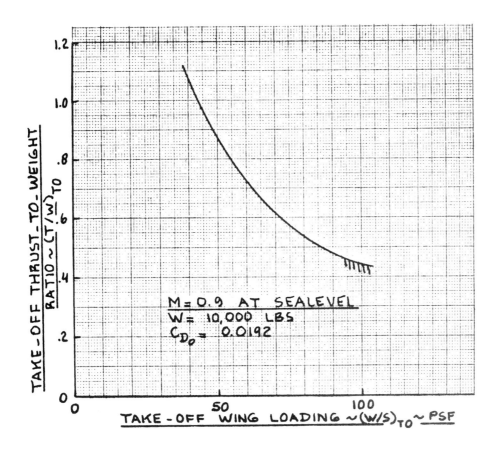

Figure 3.33 Allowable Values of Wing Loading and Thrust-
to-Weight Ratio to Meet a Given Maximum
Speed at Sealevel

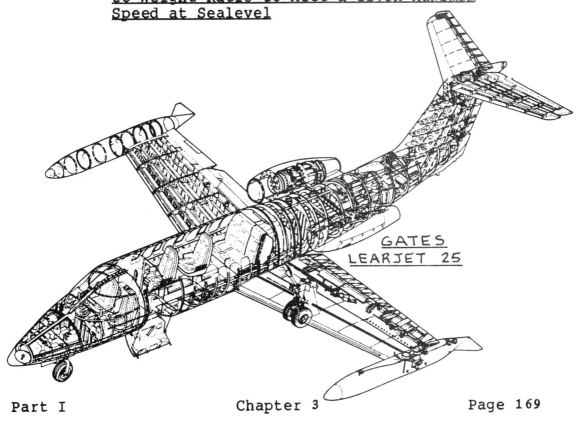

GATES
LEARJET 25

3.7 MATCHING OF ALL SIZING REQUIREMENTS AND THE APPLICATION TO THREE EXAMPLE AIRPLANES

3.7.1 Matching of all Sizing Requirements

Having established a series of relations between:

Take-off thrust-to-weight (weight-to-power) ratio,

Take-off wing loading,

Maximum required lift coefficients,

and Aspect ratio,

it is now possible to determine the 'best' combination of these quantities for the design at hand. The word 'best' is used rather than 'optimum' because the latter implies a certain mathematical precision. What is usually done at this point is to overlay all requirements and select the lowest possible thrust-to-weight ratio and the highest possible wing loading which are consistent with all requirements. This process is also known as the matching process.

Typical matching diagrams resulting from this matching process are discussed in Sub-sections 3.7.2 through 3.7.4.

3.7.2 Matching Example 1: Twin Engine Propeller Driven Airplane

Table 2.17 contains the mission specification for this airplane. To determine the allowable power and wing loadings, the landing, take-off, climb and cruise speed requirements will all be translated into ranges of allowable values for (W/S), (W/P) and $C_{L_{max}}$.

3.7.2.1 Take-off distance sizing

Table 2.17 requires $s_{G_{TO}}$ = 1,500 ft under FAR 23 rules at sealevel and for a standard day. From Eqn.(3.4) it is found that:

$$1,500 = 4.9 \ TOP_{23} + 0.009 TOP_{23}^{2}$$

This yields:

$$TOP_{23} = 218 \ hp/ft^{2}$$

Because σ = 1.0 in this case, Eqn.(3.2) yields:

$$(W/S)(W/P) = 218C_{L_{max_{TO}}}$$

Typical values for $C_{L_{max_{TO}}}$ for a twin propeller

driven airplane are seen to be 1.4 - 2.0 from Table 3.1.

For this airplane values of 1.4, 1.7 and 2.0 will be considered. The following tabulation can now be made:

$C_{L_{max_{TO}}} =$	1.4	1.7	2.0
$(W/S)_{TO}$	$(W/P)_{TO}$	$(W/P)_{TO}$	$(W/P)_{TO}$
psf	lbs/hp	lbs/hp	lbs/hp
20	15.3	18.5	21.8
30	10.2	12.4	14.5
40	7.6	9.3	10.9
50	6.1	7.4	8.7
60	5.1	6.2	7.3

Figure 3.34 shows a graphical presentation of these results.

3.7.2.2 Landing distance sizing

Table 2.17 requires that s_{G_L} = 1,500 ft under FAR 23 rules at sealevel and a standard day. From Eqn.(3.12):

$$V_{s_L}^2 = 1,500/0.265 = 5,660 \text{ kts}^2$$

Therefore:

$$V_{s_L} = 75.2 \text{ kts} = 127 \text{ fps}$$

With Eqn.(3.1) this now requires that:

$$(W/S)_L = \{(127^2 \times 0.002378)/2\}C_{L_{max_L}} = 19.2C_{L_{max_L}}$$

Table 2.17 also specified:

$$W_L = 0.95W_{TO}$$

The wing loading requirement therefore changes to:

$$(W/S)_{TO} = (19.2/0.95)C_{L_{max_L}} = 20.2C_{L_{max_L}}$$

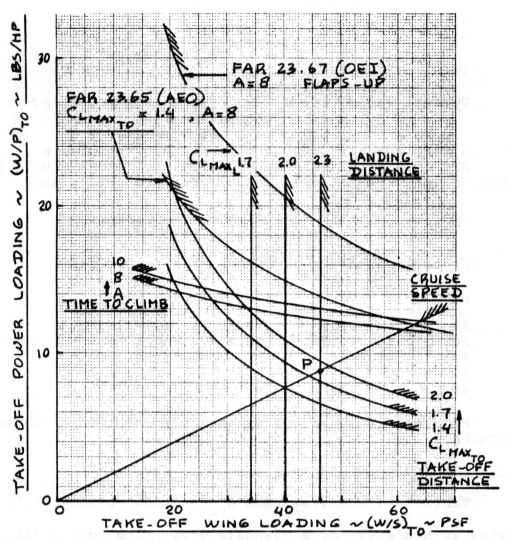

Figure 3.34 Matching Results for Sizing of a Twin Engine
Propeller Driven Airplane

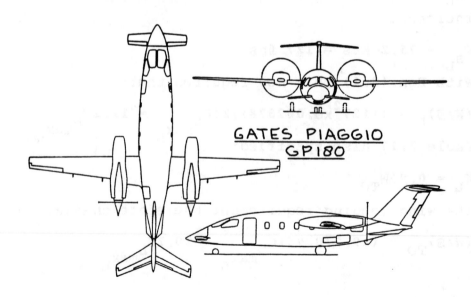

GATES PIAGGIO
GP180

From Table 3.1 it follows that typical values for $C_{L_{max_L}}$ for this type airplane are: 1.6 - 2.5.

In this case a range of values of 1.7, 2.0 and 2.3 will be considered, leading to maximum allowable wing loadings of 34.3, 40.4 and 46.5 psf respectively.

Figure 3.34 shows how this further restricts the useful range of combinations of $(W/S)_{TO}$ and $(W/P)_{TO}$.

3.7.2.3 FAR 23 climb sizing

The example in Sub-section 3.4.4 showed that for this type of airplane, the requirements of FAR 23.65 and 23.67 were the most critical. Therefore only these requirements will be considered in this example calculation.

The inexperienced reader is warned not to always take this outcome for granted. When in doubt: check all requirements!

FAR 23.65 (AEO)

As shown in Sub-section 3.4.4 the climb gradient component of this requirement was more critical than the climb rate component.

From Eqn.(3.30):

$$(18.97\eta_p\sigma^{1/2})/(W/P)(W/S)^{1/2} = \{0.0833 + (L/D)^{-1}\}/C_L^{1/2}$$

The drag polar for this airplane in the gear-up, take-off flaps configuration is found with the procedure of Sub-section 3.4.1.

From p.53, W_{TO} = 7,900 lbs. With Figure 3.22a, this yields: S_{wet} = 1,400 ft^2. Figure 3.21a shows that f = 7 ft^2 is a reasonable value for equivalent parasite area.

Using an average wing loading of 30 psf, S = 263 ft^2 and thus:

C_{D_0} = 0.0266. For take-off flaps an incremental drag coefficient of 0.0134 will be assumed. The drag polars for this airplane can be summarized as follows:

for the clean configuration: $C_D = 0.0266 + C_L^2/\pi Ae$, with e = 0.8

for take-off:
gear up $C_D = 0.0400 + C_L^2/\pi Ae$, with e = 0.8

For this airplane, aspect ratios of 8 and 10 will be considered. Values for $C_{L_{max_{TO}}}$ were taken as 1.4, 1.7

and 2.0. The corresponding 'safe' values of C_L for this

flight condition are: 1.2, 1.5 and 1.8. This yields a 'margin' of $\Delta C_L = 0.2$. With this information the

following table of L/D values can now be determined:

		A = 8		A=10	
$C_{L_{max_{TO}}}$	$C_{L_{TO}}$	(L/D)	$(L/D)^{-1}$	(L/D)	$(L/D)^{-1}$
1.4	1.2	10.8	0.093	12.3	0.081
1.7	1.5	9.9	0.101	11.6	0.086
2.0	1.8	8.9	0.112	10.7	0.094

Assuming $\eta_p = 0.0$, while $\sigma = 1.0$ it is possible

to tabulate values for W/P as follows:

	A=8			A=10		
$C_{L_{max_{TO}}}$	1.4	1.7	2.0	1.4	1.7	2.0
$(W/S)_{TO}$ psf			$(W/P)_{TO}$ lbs/hp			
20	21.1	22.6	23.3	22.6	24.6	25.7
30	17.2	18.4	19.0	18.5	20.1	21.0
40	14.9	15.9	16.5	16.0	17.4	18.2
50	13.3	14.3	14.7	14.3	15.5	16.2
60	12.2	13.0	13.5	13.1	14.2	14.8

The reader will note that for increasing A and for increasing $C_{L_{max_{TO}}}$ less power is required!

Figure 3.34 superimposes the FAR 23.65 results on results obtained from previous sizing criteria.

FAR 23.67 (OEI)

To meet this requirement the flaps may be in the most favorable position. Most favorable in this case means that position of the flaps which yields the highest value of $(C_L^{3/2}/C_D)_{max}$. The drag polars for this case are estimated as follows:

Flaps up, gear up, one
propeller feathered:
$$C_D = 0.0266 + \underset{prop.}{0.0034} + C_L^2/\pi Ae$$

Flaps take-off, gear up, one
propeller feathered:

$$C_D = 0.0266 + \underset{prop.}{0.0034} + \underset{flaps}{0.0134} + C_L^2/\pi Ae$$

The following results are now obtained:

		flaps up		flaps t.o.	
		e = 0.85		e = 0.80	
A=		8	10	8	10
$(C_L^{3/2}/C_D)_{max}$ (Eqn.(3.27))		13.6	16.1	11.8	13.9
$C_{L_{RC_{max}}}$ (Eqn.(3.25))		1.39	1.55	1.65	1.84

It is clear that the flaps up case is the more favorable one. For flaps up it was already assumed that $C_{L_{max}} = 1.7$. The lift coefficient values of 1.4 and 1.6 are reasonably compatible with this.

Next, V_{s_0} at 5,000 ft needs to be determined as a function of wing loading.

This yields: $V_{s_0} = 23.96 \ (W/S)^{1/2}$. The required value of rate of climb parameter, RCP can now be computed as follows:

$(W/S)_{TO}$	V_{s_0}	V_{s_0}	RC	RCP
				$= .027 V_{s_0}^2$ Eqn.(3.23)
psf	fps	kts	fpm	
20	107.2	63.5	109	0.00330
30	131.2	77.7	163	0.00494
40	151.5	89.8	218	0.00661
50	169.4	100.4	272	0.00824
60	185.6	110.0	327	0.00991

Equation 3.24 relates the required value of RCP to those of allowable values for W/S and W/P. For the two values of aspect ratio it can now be shown that Eqn.(3.24) yields:

For A = 8:

$$RCP = 0.8/(W/P) - (W/S)^{1/2}/239.9 \text{ and,}$$

For A = 10:

$$RCP = 0.8/(W/P) - (W/S)^{1/2}/284$$

The following tabulation can now be made:

A = 8

$(W/S)_{TO}$	$(W/S)^{1/2}/239.9$	RCP	(W/P) 5,000 ft	$(W/P)_{TO}$ sealevel
psf			lbs/hp	lbs/hp
20	0.01864	0.00330	36.5	30.7
30	0.02283	0.00494	28.8	24.2
40	0.02636	0.00661	24.3	20.4
50	0.02948	0.00824	21.2	17.8
60	0.03229	0.00991	19.0	16.0

A = 10

$(W/S)_{TO}$	$(W/S)^{1/2}/284$	RCP	(W/P) 5,000 ft	$(W/P)_{TO}$ sealevel
psf			lbs/hp	lbs/hp
20	0.01575	0.00330	42.0	35.3
30	0.01929	0.00494	33.0	27.7
40	0.02227	0.00661	27.7	23.3
50	0.02490	0.00824	24.1	20.2
60	0.02727	0.00991	21.5	18.1

Only the A = 8 requirement is shown in Figure 3.34.

It is clear, that for this airplane, the AEO climb requirement is the more critical one. Since this finding is strongly dependent on the values used for the drag polars, it should be checked as soon as more accurate estimates of the drag polars are available. Such an estimate is available as soon as the first configuration threeview of the airplane has been generated. How this can be done is the subject of Part II in this series (Ref.1).

3.7.2.4 Cruise speed sizing

The 250 kts speed requirement at 10,000 ft (Table 2.17) was used in Sub-section 3.6.3 and the results plotted in Figure 3.31. These results are now superimposed on Figure 3.34. It is seen, that this a rather critical requirement.

3.7.2.5 Time-to-climb sizing

Table 2.17 requires a 10 min. time-to-climb to 10,000 ft. It will be assumed, that h_{abs} = 25,000, which is compatible with a normally aspirated piston engine installation.

From Eqn.(3.33) it now follows that:

RC_0 = 1,277 fpm, in the clean configuration.

From Eqn.(3.23) a value for RCP is found as: 0.0387.

With Eqn.(3.27), and C_{D_0} = 0.0266 it is found that:

For A = 8: $(C_L^{3/2})/C_D$ = 13.4

For A = 10: $(C_L^{3/2})/C_D$ = 15.8

Eqn.(3.24) now yields the following results:

For A = 8 : $0.0387 = 0.8/(W/P) - (W/S)^{1/2}/255$

For A = 10: $0.0387 = 0.8/(W/P) - (W/S)^{1/2}/300$

The following tabulation can now be made:

$(W/S)_{TO}$	RCP	$(W/S)^{1/2}/255$	$(W/P)_{TO}$	$(W/S)^{1/2}/300$	$(W/P)_{TO}$
psf			lbs/hp		lbs/hp
20	0.0387	0.0175	14.2	0.0149	14.9
30	0.0387	0.0215	13.3	0.0183	14.0
40	0.0387	0.0248	12.6	0.0211	13.4
50	0.0387	0.0277	12.1	0.0236	12.8
60	0.0387	0.0304	11.6	0.0258	12.4

These time-to-climb results are also plotted in Figure 3.34.

3.7.2.6 Summary of matching results

Examining the matching requirements of Figure 3.34, Point P seems a reasonable choice. With this choice, the twin propeller driven airplane is now characterized by the following design parameters:

Take-off weight: 7,900 lbs
Empty weight: 4,900 lbs
Fuel weight: 1,706 lbs

These data were already known on p.53.

Maximum lift coefficients:

Clean: $C_{L_{max}}$ = 1.7

Take-off: $C_{L_{max_{TO}}}$ = 1.85 (Point P in Figure 3.34)

Landing: $C_{L_{max_L}}$ = 2.3 (Point P in Figure 3.34)

Aspect ratio: A = 8 is sufficient by Figure 3.34.

Take-off wing loading: 46 psf (Point P in Fig. 3.34)

Wing area: 172 ft^2

Power loading at take-off: 8.8 lbs/hp

Take-off power: 898 hp

In Part II of this text an example is given showing how a configuration can be developed on the basis of this information.

3.7.3 Matching Example 2: Jet Transport

Table 2.18 defines the mission for this airplane. Note, that the fieldlength is 5,000 ft at 5,000 ft altitude and for a 95°F day.

3.7.3.1 Take-off distance sizing

For take-off flaps a corresponding range of values of $C_{L_{max_{TO}}}$ = 1.6 to 2.2 is found from Table 3.1. For this example values of 1.6, 2.0 and 2.4 will be investigated.

Next, it is observed that at 5,000 ft, the pressure ratio δ = 0.8320. With a temperature of 95°F, the temperature ratio θ = (95 + 459.7)/518.7 = 1.0694. This yields σ = 0.8320/1.0694 = 0.7780.

From Eqn.(3.8):

$$5,000 = 37.5(W/S)\{0.7780 C_{L_{max_{TO}}} (T/W)\}^{-1}$$

After rearrangement this yields:

$$(T/W) = \{0.009640(W/S)\}/C_{L_{max_{TO}}}$$

In the latter equation, (T/W) is the same as $(T/W)_{TO}$ for the 5,000 ft, hot day condition.

The following table can now be constructed:

(W/S) psf	$C_{L_{max_{TO}}}$ =	$(T/W)_{TO}$ 5,000 ft, hot			$(T/W)_{TO}$ sealevel std.		
		1.6	2.0	2.4	1.6	2.0	2.4
60		0.36	0.29	0.24	0.42	0.34	0.28
80		0.48	0.39	0.32	0.56	0.45	0.37
100		0.60	0.48	0.40	0.70	0.56	0.47
120		0.72	0.58	0.48	0.84	0.67	0.56

x1.17

A factor of 1.17 was used to translate the 5,000 ft, hot day thrust requirement into a sealevel, standard day thrust requirement. This factor was obtained from typical turbofan data for this type of airplane.

Figure 3.35 shows the allowable combination of $(W/S)_{TO}$, $(T/W)_{TO}$ and $C_{L_{max_{TO}}}$ for which the take-off requirement is satisfied.

3.7.3.2 Landing distance sizing

From Eqns.(3.15) and (3.16) it is found that:

$$5,000 = 0.3 \times 1.69 V_{s_L}^2 = 0.507 V_{s_L}^2$$

Therefore:

$$V_{s_L}^2 = 9,862, \text{ or: } V_{s_L} = 99.3 \text{ kts.}$$

From Eqn.(3.1) this now yields:

$$V_{s_L}^2 = 2(W/S)/\rho C_{L_{max_L}}$$

At the 5,000 ft hot day condition, this results in:

$$(W/S)_L = 26.0 C_{L_{max_L}}$$

From Table 3.1 it follows that a suitable range of maximum lift coefficients in the landing configuration is: 1.8 to 2.8. For this example the values 1.8, 2.2, 2.6 and 3.0 will be investigated.

The following table can now be constructed:

$C_{L_{max_L}}$	$(W/S)_L$	$(W/S)_{TO}$	
1.8	46.8	55.1	It must be remembered
2.2	57.2	67.3	from Table 2.18 that
2.6	67.6	79.5	landing weight is 0.85x
3.0	78.0	91.8	the take-off weight.
	:0.85		

Figure 3.35 shows these results graphically.

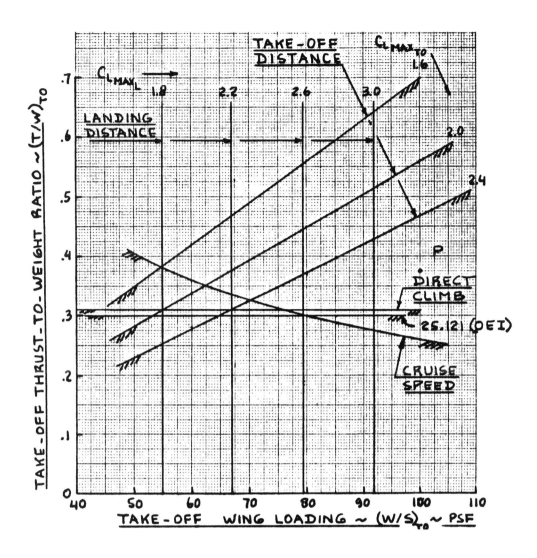

Figure 3.35 Matching Results for Sizing of a Jet Transport

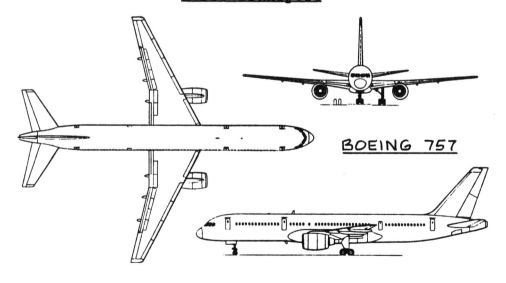

BOEING 757

3.7.3.3 FAR 25 climb sizing

For a similar transport, it was already shown in Sub-section 3.4.8, that the most critical requirement was that of FAR 25.121 (OEI). For that reason, only this requirement will be accounted for. The example in Sub-section 3.4.8 dealt with a jet transport with W_{TO} = 125,000 lbs. The airplane resulting from the specification of Table 2.18 has W_{TO} = 127,000 lbs.

This is judged to be sufficiently similar, so that the numerical results of Figure 3.25 apply. Figure 3.35 shows the FAR 25.121 (OEI) line from Figure 3.25.

3.7.3.4 Cruise speed sizing

Table 2.18 specifies a cruise speed of M = 0.82 at 35,000 ft. The low speed, clean drag polar for this airplane is roughly that of page 145:

$$C_D = 0.0184 + C_L^2/26.7, \text{ for A = 10 and e = 0.85.}$$

From Figure 3.32 the compressibility drag increment at M = 0.82 is assumed to be 0.0005. At 35,000 ft,

$$\bar{q} = 1482 \times 0.2353 \times M^2 = 234 \text{ psf.}$$

Eqn.(3.60) now yields:

$$(T/W)_{reqd} = 4.42/(W/S) + (W/S)/6,249$$

The following tabulation results from the speed sizing process:

$(W/S)_{TO}$	(T/W)	$(T/W)_{TO}$	
psf	cruise	take-off	
60	0.083	0.36	The ratio of thrust at
80	0.068	0.30	M = 0.82 at 35,000 ft to
100	0.060	0.26	that at sealevel, static
120	0.056	0.24	is roughly 0.23. This is
		:0.23	based on typical turbofan
			data for this type of
			airplane.

Figure 3.35 shows these results graphically.

3.7.3.5 Direct climb sizing

Table 2.18 specifies that direct climb to 35,000 ft at take-off gross weight must be possible. It will be assumed here, that this means that the airplane service ceiling at gross take-off weight is to be 35,000 ft. From Table 3.8 this means a climb rate of 500 fpm at 35,000 ft and in this case at M = 0.82

Eqn.(3.34) will be used in the climb sizing to this requirement. In Eqn.(3.34):

$$RC = 500/60 = 8.33 \text{ fps} \qquad V = 798 \text{ fps}$$

$$S = 127,000/100 = 1,270 \text{ ft}^2 \qquad \bar{q} = 234 \text{ psf}$$

$$C_L = 0.43 \qquad C_D = 0.0257$$

$$L/D = 16.7, \text{ so that:}$$

$$(T/W)_{reqd} = 8.33/798 + 1/16.7 = 0.07 \text{ at } 35,000 \text{ ft}$$

and at M = 0.82. Therefore, the sealevel, static value for T/W is:

$$(T/W)_{TO} = 0.07/0.23 = 0.31.$$

Figure 3.35 shows this result also.

3.7.3.6 Summary of matching results

Figure 3.35 shows that there is an interesting problem with this airplane. The take-off requirement from the relatively short field on a hot day dominates the (T/W) requirements. It will therefore be of utmost importance to develop a low drag high lift system for the take-off configuration. Trimmed values for $C_{L_{max_{TO}}}$ with existing mechanical flaps are limited to about 2.4 with a conventional configuration. With a canard or three-surface configuration it may be possible to get up to 2.8. The corresponding landing value of trimmed maximum lift coefficient is 3.2. If these numbers are selected, the matching process yields an airplane defined by point P in Figure 3.35.

It is clear, that a considerable amount of high lift development will be needed, to make this airplane viable.

If point P is accepted as a satisfactory match point, the airplane characteristics can be summarized as follows:

Take-off weight: W_{TO} = 127,000 lbs

Empty weight: W_E = 68,450 lbs

Fuel weight: W_F = 25,850 lbs

These data were already known on p.59.

Maximum lift coefficients:

Clean: $C_{L_{max}}$ = 1.4 (p.145)

Take-off: $C_{L_{max_{TO}}}$ = 2.8

Landing: $C_{L_{max_L}}$ = 3.2

Aspect ratio: 10. (Note: the reader should investigate the beneficial effect of designing toward a higher aspect ratio.)

Take-off wing loading: $(W/S)_{TO}$ = 98 psf (PointP)

Wing area: $S = 127,000/98 = 1,296$ ft^2

Take-off thrust-to-weight ratio:
$(T/W)_{TO}$ = 0.375 (Point P)

Take-off thrust: T_{TO} = 47,625 lbs

In Part II of this text an example is given of how the configuration design for this jet transport can be started with the help of the information generated in the preliminary sizing process.

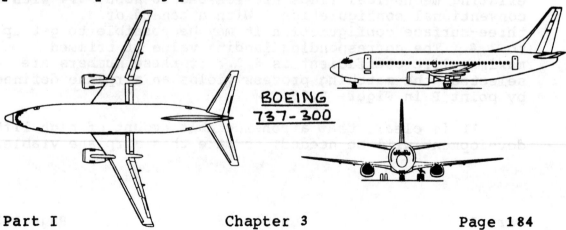

BOEING
737-300

3.7.4 Matching Example 3: Fighter

Table 2.19 defines the mission of this airplane. To determine the allowable range of wing loadings and thrust-to-weight ratios, the take-off, landing, climb and cruise speed requirements will all be translated into ranges of allowable values for $(W/S)_{TO}$, $(T/W)_{TO}$ and the various values of $C_{L_{max}}$.

3.7.4.1 Take-off distance sizing

Table 2.19 stipulates a groundrun of 2,000 ft at sealevel and for a 95°F day. It will be assumed that this take-off is from a hard surface. Ref.15 specifies: μ_G = 0.025 in that case.

On page 155 it was determined that for a 95°F day the density is: ρ = 0.002224 slugs/ft^3

Eqn.(3.9) yields:

$$2,000 = \frac{0.0447(W/S)_{TO}}{0.002224[C_{L_{max_{TO}}}\{k_2(T/W)_{TO} - 0.025\} - 0.72C_{D_0}]}$$

From p.102, with an assumed bypass ratio of λ = 3:1, k_2 = 0.75x8/7 = 0.857. From pages 154 and 155, the value of C_{D_0} without stores is:

C_{D_0} = 0.0096 + 0.0030 = 0.0126.

Therefore, the take-off distance requirement can be reduced to:

$$C_{L_{max_{TO}}}\{85.3(T/W)_{TO} - 2.49\} - 0.905 = (W/S)_{TO}$$

The following tabulation can now be made:

$(T/W)_{TO}$ 95°F	$C_{L_{max_{TO}}}$ = 1.6	1.8	2.0	$(T/W)_{TO}$ std. day
		$(W/S)_{TO}$		
0.4	50	56	62	0.47
0.6	77	87	96	0.71
0.8	104	117	131	0.94
1.0	132	148	165	1.18

A factor of 1.18 was used to translate the hot day thrust data into standard day thrust data. This factor comes from typical turbofan data for this type of airplane.

Figure 3.36 shows the graphical results.

3.7.4.2 Landing distance sizing

According to 3.3.5.1 the FAR 25 method can be used except that a correction for approach speed must be made.

Table 2.19 specifies the groundrun as < 2,400 ft. The ratio of groundrun to total distance during landing is roughly 1.9 unless special retardation precedures are used:

$$s_L = 1.9 s_{LG}$$

For this fighter therefore: $s_L = 1.9 \times 2,400 = $
$$= 4,560 \text{ ft.}$$

From Figure 3.16, $s_L = 4,560/0.6 = 7,600$ ft.

From Figure 3.17 this yields: $V_A^2 = 25,000$ kts^2.

However, since for a fighter $V_A = 1.2 V_{s_L}$ instead of $1.3 V_{s_L}$ it follows that:

$$V_A = \sqrt{25,000} = 158 \text{ kts}$$

Therefore, $V_{s_L} = 158/1.2 = 132$ kts = 222 fps.

From Eqn.(3.1):

$$222^2 = (2/0.002224)(W/S)_L / C_{L_{max_L}} \text{, or:}$$

$$(W/S)_L = 54.8 C_{L_{max_L}}$$

If it is assumed, that $W_L = 0.85 W_{TO}$ (not specified

in Table 2.19), the following tabulation can now be made:

$C_{L_{max_L}}$	$(W/S)_L$ psf	$(W/S)_{TO}$ psf
1.8	98.6	116
2.0	109.6	129
2.2	120.6	142
	:0.85	

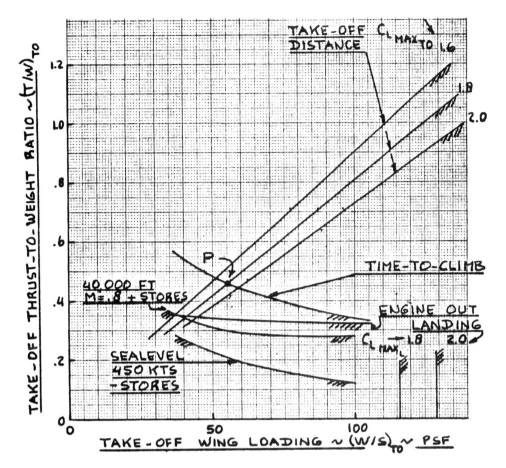

Figure 3.36 Matching Results for Sizing of a Fighter

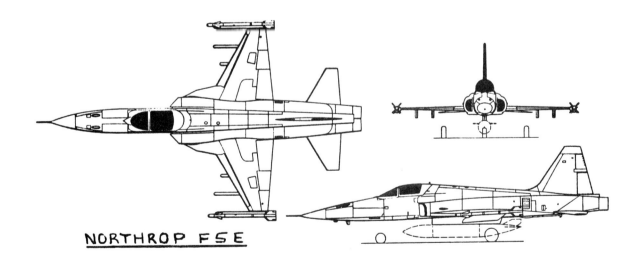

NORTHROP F5E

Figure 3.36 shows that the landing requirement is not critical in the selection of wing loading. The reason is that a 2,000 ft groundrun is very liberal for this type of a fighter.

3.7.4.3 Climb sizing

The climb performance specifications are given in Table 2.19. Examples were alreay computed in Sub-section 3.4.12 and graphically shown as requirements 1) and 2) in Figure 3.27. These lines are repeated in Figure 3.36. The reader will note that requirement 3) of Figure 3.27 is not shown in Figure 3.36 because this requirement was not a part of those listed in Table 2.19.

3.7.4.4 Cruise speed sizing

According to Table 2.19 the airplane must satisfy four different speed requirements:

At sealevel: 450 kts 'clean' and
             400 kts with external stores

At 40,000 ft: M = 0.85 'clean and
              M = 0.80 with external stores

These requirements will be subjected to the speed sizing process of Sub-section 3.6.4.

Sealevel speed sizing

The Mach numbers at these speeds are 0.68 and 0.6 respectively. It will be assumed that there are no compressibility effects at these Mach numbers. The drag polars of Sub-section 3.4.12 can therefore be used:

Low speed 'clean: $C_D = 0.0096 + 0.0995C_L^2$

Low speed + stores: $C_D = 0.0126 + 0.0995C_L^2$

Eqn.(3.60) will be used for the speed sizing. The following is found:

For 450 kts 'clean':

$(T/W) = 6.58/(W/S) + (W/S)/6,886$

This results in the following tabulation:

$(W/S)_{TO}$ with stores (psf)	(W/S) clean (psf)	(T/W) M=0.68 clean	$(T/W)_{TO}$ static clean	$(T/W)_{TO}$ with stores
40	33.8	0.20	0.32	0.27
60	50.7	0.14	0.22	0.19
80	67.6	0.11	0.17	0.15
100	84.5	0.09	0.15	0.12
x0.85		x1.65	x0.85	

For 400 kts with stores:

$$(T/W) = 6.73/(W/S) + (W/S)/5,368$$

This results in the following tabulation:

$(W/S)_{TO}$ with stores (psf)	(W/S) clean (psf)	(T/W) M=0.60 clean	$(T/W)_{TO}$ static clean	$(T/W)_{TO}$ with stores
40	33.8	0.21	0.32	0.27
60	50.7	0.14	0.22	0.18
80	67.6	0.11	0.17	0.15
100	84.5	0.10	0.15	0.12
x0.85		x1.54	x0.85	

Figure 3.36 shows the graphical results of the sealevel speed sizing.

40,000 ft speed sizing

At M = 0.8 a compressibility drag increment of 0.0020 was assumed for this airplane on p.152. At M = 0.85 a compressibility drag increment of 0.0030 will be assumed. The compressibility drag due to the stores will be neglected. This is a reasonable assumption because slender stores show no drag rise until about M = 0.9.
The following drag polars are therefore used:

at M = 0.85 'clean': $C_D = 0.0126 + 0.0995C_L^2$

at M = 0.80, + stores: $C_D = 0.0146 + 0.0995C_L^2$

Eqn.(3.60) will again be used in the speed sizing. It is found that:

For M = 0.85 'clean':

$(T/W) = 2.5/(W/S) + (W/S)/1,991$

This results in the following tabulation:

$(W/S)_{TO}$	(W/S)	(T/W)	$(T/W)_{TO}$	$(T/W)_{TO}$
with stores (psf)	clean (psf)	M=0.85 clean	static clean	with stores
40	33.8	0.09	0.40	0.33
60	50.7	0.07	0.33	0.27
80	67.6	0.07	0.31	0.26
100	84.5	0.07	0.31	0.26
x0.85			:0.23	x0.85

For M = 0.8 with stores:

$(T/W) = 2.5/(W/S) + (W/S)/1,769$

This results in the following tabulation:

$(W/S)_{TO}$	(W/S)	(T/W)	$(T/W)_{TO}$	$(T/W)_{TO}$
with stores (psf)	clean (psf)	M=0.8 clean	static clean	with stores
40	33.8	0.09	0.40	0.34
60	50.7	0.08	0.34	0.29
80	67.6	0.08	0.33	0.28
100	84.5	0.08	0.34	0.28
x0.85			:0.23	x0.85

Figure 3.36 shows the graphical results of the 40,000 ft speed sizing.

3.7.4.5 Summary of matching results

It can be seen from Figure 3.36 that the take-off requirement and the time-to-climb requirement are the critical ones. Assuming a take-off lift coefficient of $C_{L_{max_{TO}}}$ = 1.8, point P is selected as the matching point

for this fighter. Therefore, by selecting:

$$(T/W)_{TO} = 0.46,$$

$$(W/S)_{TO} = 55 \text{ psf},$$

$$C_{L_{max_{TO}}} = 1.8,$$

all requirements are met. The landing lift coefficient is seen to be not critical. Therefore it would be possible <u>not</u> to put a separate landing flap setting in the airplane.

The fighter airplane is now determined by the following characteristics:

Take-off weight with stores: 64,500 lbs
Take-off weight 'clean':   54,500 lbs
Empty weight: 33,500 lbs
Fuel weight: 18,500 lbs

These data were already known on p.67.

Maximum lift coefficients:

Clean: $C_{L_{max}}$ not determined

Take-off: $C_{L_{max_{TO}}} = 1.8$

Landing: $C_{L_{max_L}}$ not critical

Aspect ratio: 4 (The reader should carry out an analysis to see what the effect is of aspect ratios of 3.5 and 4.5).

Wing area: $64,500/55 = 1,173 \text{ ft}^2$

Thrust at take-off: $T_{TO} = 64,500 \times 0.46 = 29,670 \text{ lbs}$

In part II of this text an example is given of how the configuration design for this fighter airplane can be started with this information.

3.8. PROBLEMS

1) For the regional transport of Section 2.8, problem 2, do the take-off, climb and landing sizing according to FAR 25 requirements.

2) For the high altitude loiter and reconnaissance airplane of Section 2.8, problem 3, perform the take-off, climb and landing sizing to FAR 25 requirements.

3) For the homebuilt airplane of Section 2.8, problem 4, carry out the take-off, climb and landing sizing to FAR 23 requirements.

4) For the supersonic cruise airplane of Section 2.8, problem 5, do the take-off, climb and landing sizing to FAR 25 requirements.

5) Do the FAR 23 sizing for an agricultural airplane with the following (sealevel only) mission requirements:

* spray or dust load of 4,000 lbs.
* ferry distance is 10 miles.
* ferry speed should be 160 mph.
* swath turn-around must be less than 20 sec.
* load dispersal rate is 45 lbs per acre.
* swath width must be 80 ft.
* speed while spraying should be 100 mph.
* take-off distance to a 50 ft obstacle must be less than 1,500 ft.
* fuel reserves after emptying the hopper must be sufficient for 20 min. at 160 mph.

6) Do the FAR 25 sizing for a 90 passenger, twin engine turboprop with the following mission:

* range 1,500 n.m. at M = 0.7 and 30,000 ft.
* crew: two pilots and three flight attendants.
* assume 200 lbs per person, including baggage.
* fieldlength 7,000 ft. for a standard day at 9,000 ft altitude.
* engine-out service ceiling: 16,000 ft.
* maximum approach speed less than 130 kts.
* fuel reserves per FAR Part 121.

7) For the fighter of Table 2.19, determine the relation between T/W and W/S at take-off if the airplane must pull sustained level turns with load factors of 4, 6 and 8. Do a trade study of the effect of maximum lift coefficient values of 1.0, 1.2 and 1.4. All this at sealevel and M = 0.8.

4. A USER'S GUIDE TO PRELIMINARY AIRPLANE SIZING

The process of preliminary airplane sizing to a variety of mission and certification requirements was discussed in detail in chapters 2 and 3.

In this chapter a step-by-step guide is provided to help guide the reader through the maze of sizing methods.

Step 1. Obtain a mission specification and construct from it a mission profile. Example mission profiles are given in Tables 2.17, 2.18 and 2.19.

Step 2. Number the mission phases in sequence, as shown in the examples of Tables 2.17 through 2.19.

Step 3. For certain mission phases the fuel fraction can be estimated directly from Table 2.1. For other mission phases, estimate the corresponding L/D and sfc values. Table 2.2 can be used as a guide.

Step 4. Determine the overall mission fuel fraction, M_{ff} with the method of Section 2.4: Eqn.(2.13).

Step 5. From the mission specification determine the fuel reserves, $W_{F_{res}}$ or the fuel reserve fraction, M_{res}.

Step 6. Follow the step-by-step procedures outlined as steps 1-7 of page 7.

Note: if the mission demands dropping of weights (such as in many military missions) some of the fuel fractions need to be corrected for this. The procedure for doing this is illustrated in Sub-section 2.6.3.

At the termination of Step 6, the following information is available for the airplane:

Take-off weight, W_{TO}

Empty weight, W_E

Fuel weight, W_F

Payload and crew weights, W_{PL} and W_{crew}, follow from the mission specification.

Step 7. Note from the mission specification what the certification base is for the airplane: homebuilt, FAR 23, FAR 25 or military. If a homebuilt is being considered, FAR 23 should be used for further preliminary sizing.

Step 8. Make a list of performance parameters to which the airplane must be sized. Such a list can be put together from the mission specification and from the certification base. The following examples are discussed in Chapter 3:

3.1 Sizing to stall speed requirements.
3.2 Sizing to take-off distance requirements.
3.3 Sizing to landing distance requirements.
3.4 Sizing to climb requirements.
3.5 Sizing to maneuvering requirements.
3.6 Sizing to cruise speed requirements.

Step 9. Perform the sizing calculations in accordance with the methods of Sections 3.1 through 3.6. This involves estimating a drag polar. This can be done rapidly with the method of Sub-section 3.4.1.

Step 10. Construct a sizing matching graph for all performance sizing requirements. Examples for constructing such matching graphs are presented in Section 3.7.

Step 11. From the matching graph select:

1) Take-off power loading: $(W/P)_{TO}$ or

   Take-off thrust-to-weight ratio: $(T/W)_{TO}$

2) Take-off wing loading: $(W/S)_{TO}$

3) Maximum (clean) lift coefficient: $C_{L_{max}}$

4) Maximum take-off lift coefficient: $C_{L_{max_{TO}}}$

5) Maximum landing lift coefficient: $C_{L_{max_L}}$

6) Wing aspect ratio: A

Step 12. Determine the take-off power, P_{TO} or the take-off thrust, T_{TO} from:

$$P_{TO} = W_{TO}/(W/P)_{TO} \text{ or from:}$$

$$T_{TO} = W_{TO}(T/W)_{TO}$$

Step 13. Determine the wing area, S from:

$$S = W_{TO}/(W/S)_{TO}$$

All airplane parameters needed to begin the development of a configuration are now defined. Part II of this book, (Ref.1) presents a methodology for the selection and layout of a preliminary airplane configuration.

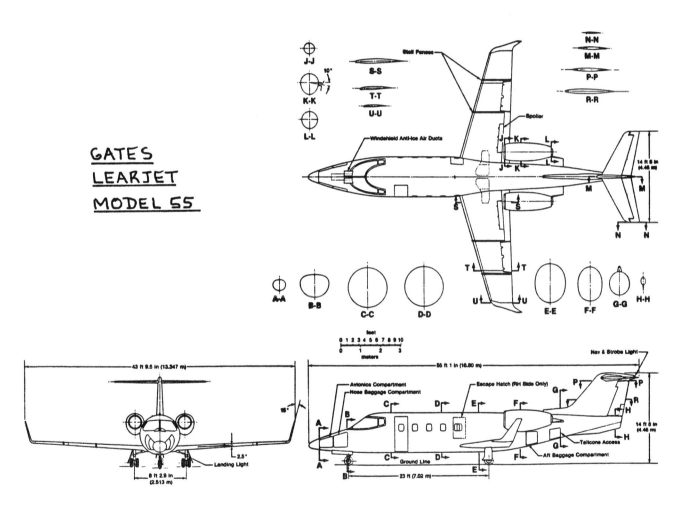

GATES LEARJET MODEL 55

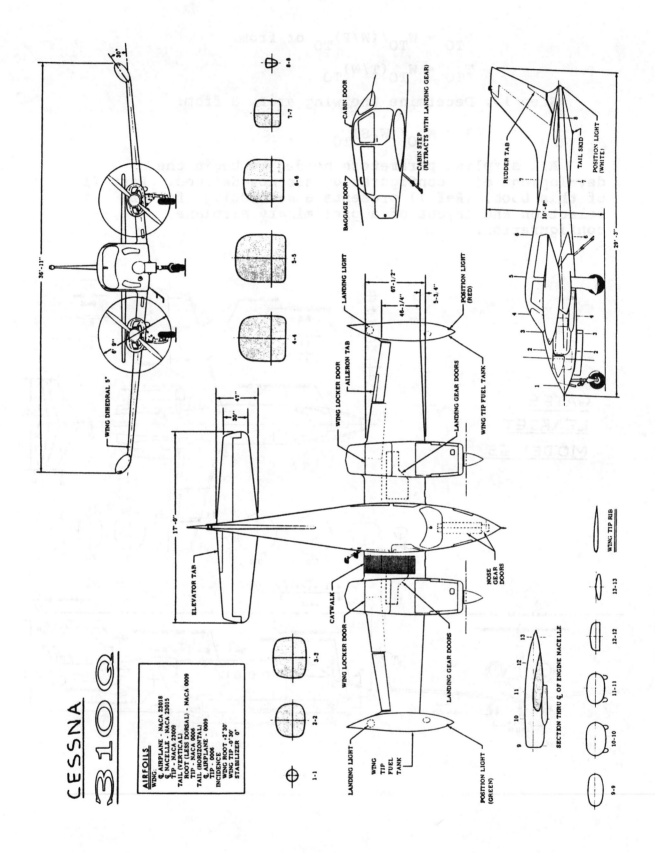

CESSNA 310Q

AIRFOILS

WING:
℄ AIRPLANE - NACA 23018
℄ NACELLE - NACA 23015
TIP - NACA 23009
TAIL (VERTICAL):
ROOT (LESS DORSAL) - NACA 0009
TIP - NACA 0006
TAIL (HORIZONTAL):
℄ AIRPLANE - 0009
TIP - 0006
INCIDENCE
WING ROOT +2°30'
WING TIP -0°30'
STABILIZER 0°

WING DIHEDRAL 5°

36'-11"

6'-9"

30°

1-1

2-2   3-2

3-3

4-4

5-5

6-6

7-7

8-8

ELEVATOR TAB

17'-0"

30"   47"

CATWALK

WING LOCKER DOOR

WING LOCKER DOOR

AILERON TAB

LANDING LIGHT

67-1/2"

46-1/4"

5-3.4"

POSITION LIGHT (RED)

LANDING GEAR DOORS

WING TIP FUEL TANK

NOSE GEAR DOORS

LANDING GEAR DOORS

LANDING LIGHT

WING TIP FUEL TANK

POSITION LIGHT (GREEN)

CABIN DOOR

CABIN STEP (RETRACTS WITH LANDING GEAR)

BAGGAGE DOOR

RUDDER TAB

TAIL SKID

POSITION LIGHT (WHITE)

10'-6"

29'-3"

WING TIP RIB

13-13

12-12

11-11

10-10

9-9

SECTION THRU ℄ OF ENGINE NACELLE

5. REFERENCES
=============

1. Roskam, J., Airplane Design: Part II, Preliminary Configuration Design and Integration of the Propulsion System.

2. Roskam, J., Airplane Design: Part III, Layout Design of Cockpit, Fuselage, Wing and Empennage: Cutaways and Inboard Profiles.

3. Roskam, J., Airplane Design: Part IV, Layout Design of Landing Gear and Systems.

4. Roskam, J., Airplane Design: Part V, Component Weight Estimation.

5. Roskam, J., Airplane Design: Part VI, Preliminary Calculation of Aerodynamic, Thrust and Power Characteristics.

6. Roskam, J., Airplane Design: Part VII, Determination of Stability, Control and Performance Characteristics: FAR and Military Requirements.

7. Roskam, J., Airplane Design: Part VIII, Airplane Cost Estimation and Optimization: Design, Development Manufacturing and Operating.

Note: These books are all published by: Roskam Aviation and Engineering Corporation, Rt4, Box 274, Ottawa, Kansas, 66067, Tel. 913-2421624.

8. Anon., Federal Aviation Regulations, Department of Transportation, Federal Aviation Administration, Distribution Requirements Section, M-482.2, Washington, D.C., 20590.

9. Taylor, J.W.R., Jane's All The World Aircraft, Published Annually by: Jane's Publishing Company, 238 City Road, London EC1V 2PU, England. (Issues used: 1945/46, 1968/84)

10. Nicolai, L.M., Fundamentals of Aircraft Design, METS, Inc., 6520 Kingsland Court, CA, 95120.

11. Loftin, Jr., L.K., Subsonic Aircraft: Evolution and the Matching of Size to Performance, NASA Reference Publication 1060, 1980.

12. Kohlman, D.L., Introduction to V/STOL Airplanes, Iowa State University Press, Ames, Iowa, 50010, 1981.

13. McCormick, B.W., Aerodynamics of V/STOL Flight, Academic Press, New York, 1967.

14. Lan, C.E. and Roskam, J., Airplane Aerodynamics and Performance, Roskam Aviation and Engineering Corp., Rt4, Box 274, Ottawa, KS, 66067, 1981.

15. MIL-C-005011B(USAF), Military Specification, Charts: Standard Aircraft Characteristics and Performance, Piloted Aircraft (Fixed Wing), June 1977.

16. Torenbeek, E., Synthesis of Subsonic Airplane Design, Kluwer Boston Inc., Hingham, Maine, 1982.

17. Roskam, J., Rapid Sizing Method for Airplanes, Journal of Aircraft, Vol.23, No.7, p.554-560, July 1986.

18. Ekvall, J.C. and Chellman, D.J., Evaluation of Aluminum-Lithium Alloys in Compression-Stiffened Aircraft Structures, Journal of Aircraft, Vol.25, No.11, p. 1001-1008, November 1988.

19. Gunnink, J.W., Design Studies of Primary Aircraft Structures in ARALL Laminates, Journal of Aircraft, Vol.25, No.11, p.1023-1032, November 1988.

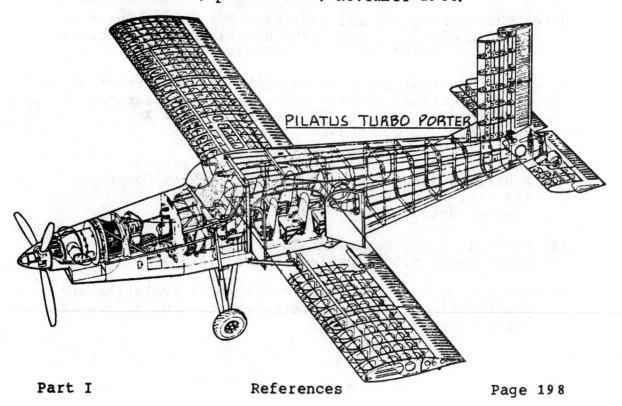

PILATUS TURBO PORTER

6. INDEX
========

APPENDIX A: COMMENTS ON THE CONVERGENCE PROPERTIES OF THE
WEIGHT SIZING METHOD OF CHAPTER 2

It is shown in Chapter 2, page 69, Eqn.(2.24) that the airplane take-off weight, W_{TO} may be estimated from

the following logarithmic equation:

$$\log_{10}W_{TO} = A + B\log_{10}(CW_{TO} - D) \qquad (A1)$$

where: A is a regression (intercept) coefficient which is determined from actual data on existing airplanes which must belong to the same general type as the airplane being sized.

   B is a regression (slope) coefficient which is determined in a manner similar to A.

   NOTE: Table 2.15 lists the numerical values for A and B for twelve types of airplanes.

   C is a coefficient which is a function of the fuel used and the fuel reserve required for any given mission. It may be computed from Eqns (2.22) and (2.13).

   D is the sum of crew weight and payload weight.

If the l.h.s and the r.h.s. of Eqn.(A1) are considered to be functions of W_{TO} it is possible to obtain a

graphical solution as shown in Figure A1. When such a solution exists, the sizing method is said to converge. The purpose of this appendix is to investigate the conditions for which convergence will or will not occur.

It is shown in Ref.17 that the existence of a solution depends on the behavior of the function:

$$\Delta = \{(\log_{10}W_{TO}) - A - B\log_{10}(CW_{TO} - D)\} \qquad (A2)$$

There are three possibilities which must be examined:

   a. Δ has NO minimum and NO maximum (i.e. no optimum)
   b. Δ has a negative minimum value
   c. Δ has a positive minimum value

Figure A2 shows a graphical representation for each.

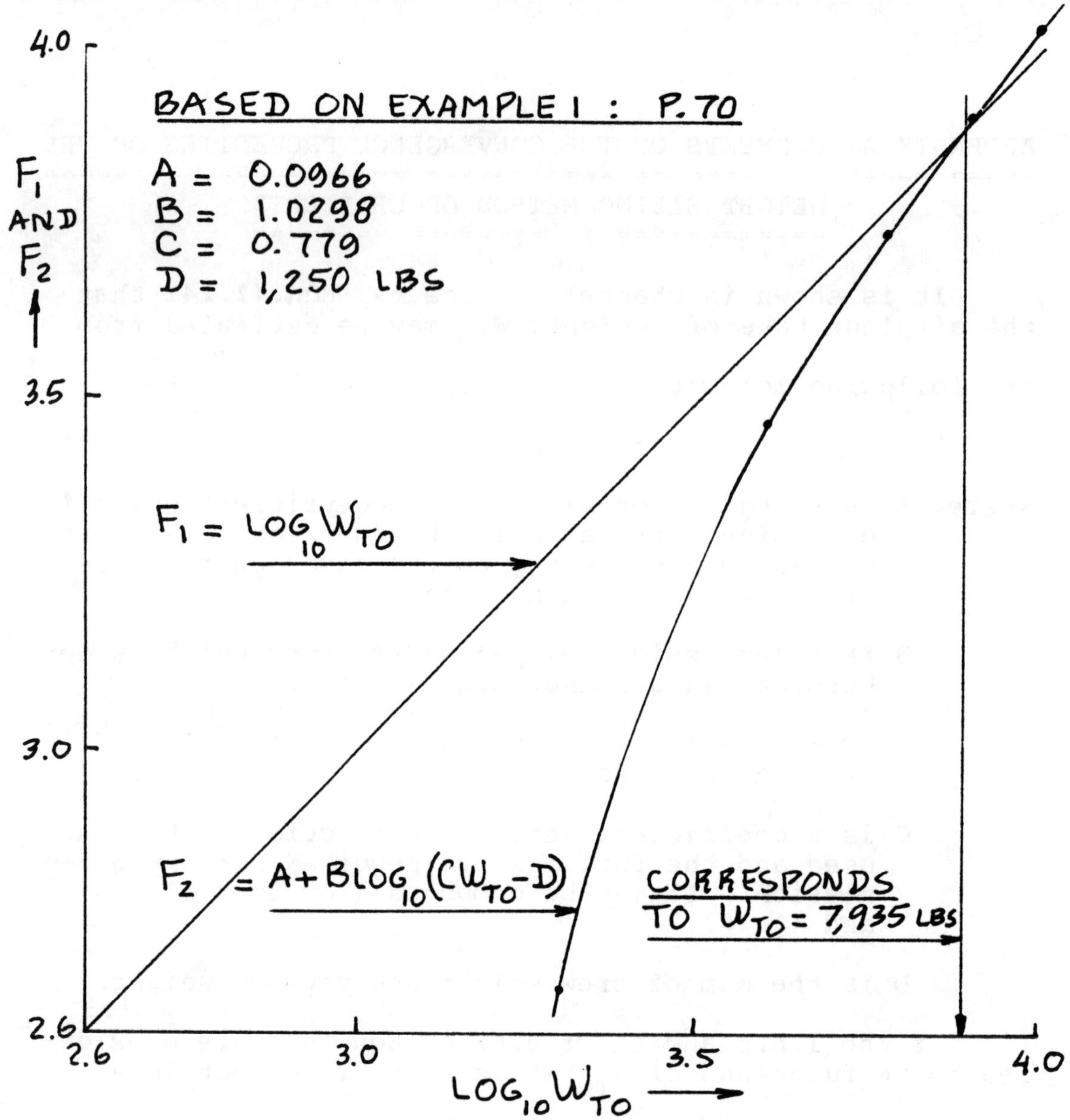

BASED ON EXAMPLE I : P. 70
A = 0.0966
B = 1.0298
C = 0.779
D = 1,250 LBS
F1 AND F2
$F_1 = LOG_{10} W_{TO}$
$F_2 = A + B LOG_{10}(CW_{TO} - D)$
CORRESPONDS TO W_{TO} = 7,935 LBS
4.0
3.5
3.0
2.6
2.6
3.0
3.5
4.0
$LOG_{10} W_{TO}$

Figure A1 Graphical Solution of Equation (A1)

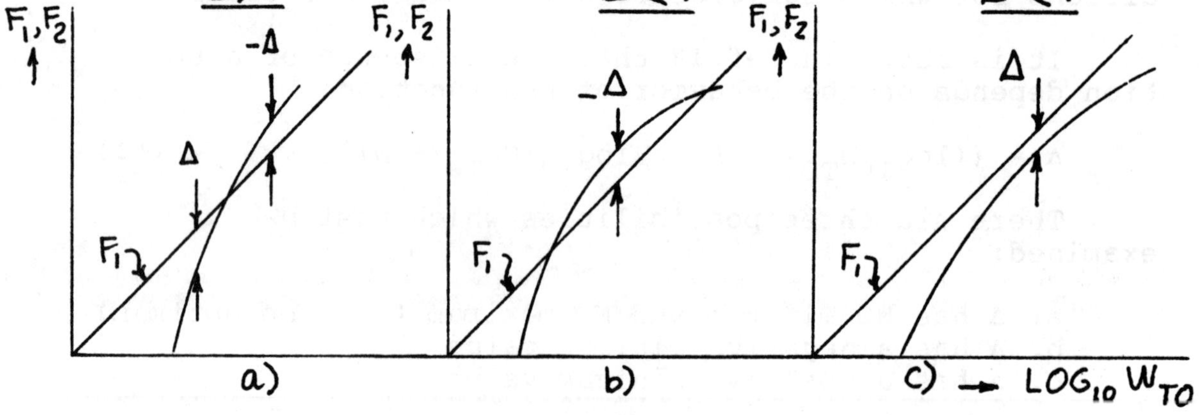

B>1
B<1
B<1
F1, F2
F1, F2
F1, F2
Δ
-Δ
-Δ
Δ
F1
F1
F1
a)
b)
c)
$LOG_{10} W_{TO}$

Figure A2 Three Possibilities for the Function Δ of Equation (A2)

If an optimum value for Δ exists, it must satisfy:

$$\partial\Delta/\partial W_{TO} = 0 \tag{A3}$$

This can be shown to occur for:

$$W_{TO} = D/C(1 - B) \tag{A4}$$

A practical optimum for Δ exists only if $B < 1.0$. Therefore, the following conclusions can be drawn:

1. If $B > 1.0$ the function Δ has no optimum (i.e. No minimum and NO maximum). This implies that only one solution exists for W_{TO} in Eqn.(A1).

   Figure A1 and Figure A2a exemplify this behavior.

2. If $B < 1.0$ the function Δ has either a maximum or a minimum. The optimum value for Δ can be determined by substituting Eqn.(A4) into Eqn.(A2). This yields:

   $$\Delta_{optimum} = \log_{10}\{D/C(1 - B)\} - A +$$
   $$- B\log_{10}[\{D/(1 - B) - D\}] \tag{A5}$$

   The following possibilities present themselves:

   2a) If $\Delta_{optimum} < 0$ there will be two solutions for W_{TO}!! Only the lower value should be given practical significance. Figure A2b illustrates this case.

   2b) If $\Delta_{optimum} > 0$ there will be NO solutions for W_{TO}: the design process does not converge! Figure A2c illustrates this case.

It is seen that whether or not cases 2a or 2b occur will depend (for any given values of A, B and D) on the value of C as found from Eqn.(2.22). Since C depends strongly on the mission fuel requirements (and therefore on the range and/or endurance requirements) it should always be possible to 'invent' a mission specification for which convergence does not occur. In such a case no airplane can be designed to meet the intended mission.

For the reason just given, it does not seem to make sense that for airplanes with B < 1.0 convergence will always occur. The reason for this anomalie may be explained as follows:

Table 2.15 shows typical values found for B for a range of airplane types. Some are > 1.0 and some are < 1.0. It must be kept in mind that values for B were determined from a regression analysis over a range of empty weights and takeoff weights for _existing_ airplanes in any given airplane category. it is therefore not sound to use the method of Eqn.(A1) {or Eqn.(2.24)} too far outside the range of airplane weight data upon which the regression analysis is based. Each structural material has specific strength and fatigue limitations. It is to be expected that if weight data were available for sufficiently high weight airplanes in each category, B would always be found as smaller than 1.0. The existence of a solution for W_{TO} would then depend only on the magnitude of C. Eqns (2.22) and (2.13) show that the value of C depends on the mission fuel needed to fly a given mission. Therefore, the takeoff weight sizing method of Eqn.(A1) would not converge for missions with extreme fuel requirements.

It is of interest to examine what becomes of W_{TO} for the case that B = 1.0 exactly! From Eqn.(A1) it can be shown that an explicit solution for W_{TO} is found from:

$$W_{TO} = D(10^A)/\{C(10^A) - 1\} \tag{A6}$$

As may be seen, a solution for W_{TO} will exist only (in the practical sense!) when the condition:

$$C > 10^{-A} \tag{A7}$$

is satisfied. For any given value of the regression coefficient A it is always possible (when B = 1.0) to 'invent' a mission specification which results in a small enough value of C so that (A7) is violated. Very long range requirements and/or very long endurance requirements will assure that this will happen!

APPENDIX B: A METHOD TO DETERMINE A VALUE FOR THE REGRES-
===
SION (INTERCEPT) COEFFICIENT 'A' FOR NEW
=====================================
STRUCTURAL MATERIALS
====================

The purpose of this appendix is to determine the effect of new structural materials on the regression (intercept) coefficient A of Equations (2.16) and (2.24).

First, an estimate for airplane empty weight, W_E

should be made using the method implied by Eqn.(2.16) on page 18. This empty weight is that weight which would be expected for an airplane with a primary structure manufactured from conventional (aluminum based) materials.

Second, it will be assumed that the reader has read the caution note on page 18 and that Table 2.16 has been used to find at a 'new' value for airplane empty weight, $W_{E_{new}}$ corresponding to whatever use is expected to be made of 'new' materials such as composites, Al-Li or ARALL.

The following notation is now introduced:

$$W_{E_{new}} = \eta W_{E_{old}} \tag{B1}$$

where: $W_{E_{old}}$ is the same as W_E obtained from Eqn.(2.16).

The assumption will be made that the regression (slope) coefficient B will not be affected by the change in materials. Thus, the 'new' value of A is found from:

$$A_{new} = A - B\log_{10}\eta \tag{B2}$$

<u>Notes</u>:

1. Since $0 < \eta < 1.0$, $A_{new} > A$!! This means that the 'new material' line representing empty weight versus takeoff weight is shifted to the right relative to the 'old' ones in Figures 2.3 through 2.14. This has the effect of lowering the empty weight for any given takeoff weight.

2. References 18 and 19 are recommended for estimating the weight reductions which can be obtained with the new materials Al-Li and ARALL respectively.

Notes

Notes

Notes

Airplane Design & Analysis Textbook Descriptions

All textbooks can be ordered from our on-line store at www.darcorp.com.

Airplane Aerodynamics & Performance
C.T. Lan & Jan Roskam

The atmosphere • basic aerodynamic principles and applications • airfoil theory • wing theory • airplane drag • airplane propulsion systems • propeller theory • fundamentals of flight mechanics for steady symmetrical flight • climb performance and speed • take-off and landing performance • range and endurance • maneuvers and flight

ISBN 1-884885-44-6

Airplane Flight Dynamics & Automatic Flight Controls Part I
Jan Roskam

General steady and perturbed state equations of motion for a rigid airplane • concepts and use of stability & control derivatives • physical and mathematical explanations of stability & control derivatives • solutions and applications of the steady state equations of motion from a viewpoint of airplane analysis and design • emphasis on airplane trim, take-off rotation and engine-out control • open loop transfer functions • analysis of fundamental dynamic modes: phugoid, short period, roll, spiral and dutch roll • equivalent stability derivatives and the relation to automatic control of unstable airplanes • flying qualities and the Cooper-Harper scale: civil and military regulations • extensive numerical data on stability, control and hingemoment derivatives

ISBN 1-884885-17-9

Airplane Flight Dynamics & Automatic Flight Controls Part II
Jan Roskam

Elastic airplane stability and control coefficients and derivatives • method for determining the equilibrium and manufacturing shape of an elastic airplane • subsonic and supersonic numerical examples of aeroelasticity effects on stability & control derivatives • bode and root-locus plots with open and closed loop airplane applications, and coverage of inverse applications • stability augmentation systems: pitch dampers, yaw dampers and roll dampers • synthesis concepts of automatic flight control modes: control-stick steering, auto-pilot hold, speed control, navigation and automatic landing • digital control systems using classical control theory applications with Z-transforms • applications of classical control theory • human pilot transfer functions

ISBN 1-884885-18-7

Airplane Design Part I
Preliminary Sizing of Airplanes
Jan Roskam

Estimating take-off gross weight, empty weight and mission fuel weight • sensitivity studies and growth factors • estimating wing area • take-off thrust and maximum clean, take-off and landing lift • sizing to stall speed, take-off distance, landing distance, climb, maneuvering and cruise speed requirements • matching of all performance requirements via performance matching diagrams

ISBN 978-1-884885-42-6

Airplane Design Part II
Preliminary Configuration Design and Integration of the Propulsion System
Jan Roskam

Selection of the overall configuration • design of cockpit and fuselage layouts • selection and integration of the propulsion system • Class I method for wing planform design • Class I method for verifying clean airplane maximum lift coefficient and for sizing high lift devices • Class I method for empennage sizing and disposition, control surface sizing and disposition, landing gear sizing and disposition, weight and balance analysis, stability and control analysis and drag polar determination

ISBN 1-884885-43-8

DARcorporation

Design • Analysis • Research

1440 Wakarusa Drive, Suite 500, Lawrence, Kansas 66049, USA - Tel: (785) 832-0434 - Fax: (785) 832-0524

info@darcorp.com – www.darcorp.com

Airplane Design & Analysis Textbook Descriptions

All textbooks can be ordered from our on-line store at www.darcorp.com.

Airplane Design Part III
Layout Design of Cockpit, Fuselage, Wing and Empennage: Cutaways and Inboard Profiles
Jan Roskam

Cockpit (or flight deck) layout design • aerodynamic design considerations for the fuselage layout • interior layout design of the fuselage • fuselage structural design considerations • wing aerodynamic and operational design considerations • wing structural design considerations • empennage aerodynamic and

operational design considerations • empennage structural and integration design consideration • integration of propulsion system • preliminary structural arrangement, material selection and manufacturing breakdown
ISBN 1-884885-56-X

Airplane Design Part IV
Layout Design of Landing Gear and Systems
Jan Roskam

Landing gear layout design • weapons integration and weapons data • flight control system layout data • fuel system layout design • hydraulic system design • electrical system layout design • environmental control system layout design • cockpit

instrumentation, flight management and avionics system layout design • de-icing and anti-icing system layout design • escape system layout design • water and waste systems layout design • safety and survivability considerations
ISBN 1-884885-53-5

Airplane Design Part V
Component Weight Estimation
Jan Roskam

Class I methods for estimating airplane component weights and airplane inertias • Class II methods for estimating airplane component weights, structure weight, powerplant weight, fixed equipment weight and airplane inertias • methods for constructing v-n diagrams • Class II

weight and balance analysis • locating component centers of gravity
ISBN 1-884885-50-0

Airplane Design Part VI
Preliminary Calculation of Aerodynamic, Thrust, and Power Characteristics
Jan Roskam

Summary of drag causes and drag modeling • Class II drag polar prediction methods •airplane drag data • installed power and thrust prediction methods • installed power and thrust data • lift and pitching moment prediction methods • airplane high lift data • methods for estimating stability, control and hingemoment derivatives • stability and

control derivative data
ISBN 1-884885-52-7

Airplane Design Part VII
Determination of Stability, Control, and Performance Characteristics: FAR and Military Requirements
Jan Roskam

Controllability, maneuverability and trim • static and dynamic stability • ride and comfort characteristics • performance prediction methods • civil and military airworthiness regulations for airplane performance and stability and control • the airworthiness code and the relationship between failure states, levels of performance and levels of flying qualities

ISBN 1-884885-54-3

Airplane Design Part VIII
Airplane Cost Estimation: Design, Development, Manufacturing, and Operating
Jan Roskam

Cost definitions and concepts • method for estimating research, development, test and evaluation cost • method for estimating prototyping cost • method for estimating manufacturing and acquisition cost • method for estimating operating cost • example of life cycle cost calculation for a military airplane • airplane design optimization and

design-to-cost considerations • factors in airplane program decision making
ISBN 1-884885-55-1

DARcorporation
Design • Analysis • Research
1440 Wakarusa Drive, Suite 500, Lawrence, Kansas 66049, USA - Tel: (785) 832-0434 - Fax: (785) 832-0524
info@darcorp.com – www.darcorp.com